"You can't r...
feel in your debt."

Melissa lifted her chin toward Ryan Trevelyan in angry disdain. Even if her mother did owe him an enormous amount of money, he still had no right to be so presumptuous.

He jerked her nearer, his face inches from her own hot cheeks. "I never do anything for nothing," he ground out, "not unless it suits me, and in your case it definitely doesn't. But as far as repayment goes, you can take your time...I can wait until you're good and ready."

Beneath his hands she suddenly trembled, not quite understanding his meaning, only the clear impression that he wouldn't wait forever.

"You'll never get anything from me!" Melissa almost shouted. She was determined to resist, to harden her will—and her heart.

Other titles by

MARGARET PARGETER

IN HARLEQUIN PRESENTS

Other titles by

MARGARET PARGETER

IN HARLEQUIN ROMANCES

Many of these titles, and other titles in the Harlequin
Romance series, are available at your local book-
seller. For a free catalogue listing all available
Harlequin Presents and Harlequin Romances, send
your name and address to:

HARLEQUIN READER SERVICE,
M.P.O. Box 707,
Niagara Falls, N.Y. 14302

Canadian address:
Stratford, Ontario, Canada N5A 6W2

portant. The fire crackled and leapt, as if its wide surrounds could scarcely contain it, but otherwise there was no sound apart from the wild shrieking of the wind.

Unable to resist, she moved nearer to the fire. There was no sign of anyone, other than the man who had brought her here, but he couldn't surely live in a house this size alone? Eagerly she held out cold hands to the yellow blaze, her mind emptied of everything but the wonderful feeling of warmth. She kept her eyes averted from the tall, looming figure beside her.

'Are you wet?'

His sardonic manner aroused her anger again, but she managed to keep it in check. 'Not really,' she said evenly, keeping her eyes on the fire.

'The ends of your coat are, I can see.' His voice was crisp and authoritative, bringing her head up with a jerk. As clouded green eyes met dark brown ones for the first time the air between them seemed charged with a peculiar tension. Melissa felt suddenly so shaken she dared not think about it and was relieved when, with an indifferent shrug, he turned away.

Dazed, she watched as he began removing his outdoor things. A duffle coat was twisted carelessly from wide shoulders to reveal a thick sweater underneath. The dark trousers were shabby, she noticed, but well tailored to his powerful length of limb. There didn't appear to be an ounce of superfluous flesh on him anywhere, yet he could never be called thin.

Finally he stooped to undo the laces of his strapped rubber boots. 'I think you would feel better if you did likewise, Miss—whoever you are?' he drawled.

Melissa almost gasped in alarm, feeling devastatingly exposed to worse than the elements. She felt like someone whose protective armour had been whipped ruthlessly away. 'So you know—knew!'

He said, brutally frank, 'Not until I leant across you to open the car door. Some aspects of the feminine form are difficult to disguise at such close quarters.'

'For one with experience!' she exclaimed impulsively, before she could stop herself.

'Sure,' again he shrugged, as if he didn't give a damn what she thought. He swept his hat from his head, tossing it on top of his discarded coat before turning to face her.

Blinking a little, in shattered astonishment, Melissa saw he was very good-looking in a rugged, entirely masculine sort of way. He had dark eyes and hair, a squarish, determined-looking chin to complement a firm but sensuous mouth. A mouth, Melissa thought with an instinctive shudder, that might be capable of teaching a girl all kinds of things she'd rather not know!

Her breath catching, she pulled herself up, wondering where such bizarre ideas came from. She wasn't even romantically inclined. She knew she was good to look at, but men left her cold. Cold and contemptuous of their wandering hands and smooth tongues, being well aware that had she been plain they would never have looked at her twice.

Yet for all her former indifference this man seemed to be affecting her strangely. She felt embarrassed and shaken out of all proportion that he had, merely by leaning over her, known she was a girl. 'I see,' she replied carefully, to his raised, waiting brows, wondering why it should be so difficult to sound cool. She was further aggravated to feel hot colour flaring wildly in her smooth cheeks, especially when blushing had never been one of her failings. Why should she begin now? 'When you first came across me,' she said quickly, trying to hide her confusion, 'you thought I was a boy.'

'I'm afraid it never occurred to me that a girl would be out in such weather,' he said curtly. 'My mistake was understandable. Perhaps now you might remove your disguise and let me have a proper look at you?' His impatient glance flicked her thick scarf and woollen helmet. 'I don't think I know you?'

Why should he sound so convinced? Reluctantly she

untied the scarf, conscious that he was staring at her intently, as if she were doing the dance of the seven veils. Indignant, she would liked to have turned her back on him, but knew it would only be foolish. As her headgear came off her hair fell, like a cloud of living flame about her shoulders. It was dark red, memorable with glowing colour, a colour which contrasted beautifully with the creamy paleness of her flawless skin and green eyes.

'Now—the coat.' Without once taking his eyes from her he gave the order abruptly, his expression curiously like that of an artist studying the assembling of a picture.

Funnily enough Melissa didn't think of disobeying. It was as if she was controlled by the power emanating from him. For the first time in her twenty years she recognised a man with considerable strength of character. Much stronger than her own. Off came her thin coat, but slowly, as she regretted her shabby clothes. How she wished she had swallowed her silly pride and not left most of her smart wardrobe in the Midlands.

Shabby or not, he seemed impressed as she stood defiantly before him. Imperceptibly his hand went out to touch her hair, to trail down her cheek. Where it stopped, on her fine jawline, his gaze took over, his eyes sliding expressionlessly to where the pronounced curves of her slender body thrust delicately against the tightness of her sweater, then on to her narrow, girlish hips and long, slim legs. The hems of her jeans might be worn and frayed but they didn't conceal the fact that there was something very shapely inside them.

Her chin lifted suddenly to shake off his lean fingers, her teeth clenching rigidly under his narrow speculation. 'Haven't you ever seen a girl before?' she heard herself asking disdainfully.

'A few,' his eyes returned to her face cynically, 'but not in the immediate vicinity, and certainly none like you. Where exactly do you live?'

'I'd rather not say.'

'Indeed?' A slightly amused smile crossed his lips. 'Is there any reason for such secrecy? Or are you so pursued by would-be suitors that you dare not reveal your address or identity?'

'Don't be silly!' She bit her lip, glad when his interest appeared to transfer itself to more practical matters. He turned away to push a large old kettle towards the heart of the fire before bending to adjust the heat.

Beneath her lashes she watched him, unable, for any good reason she could think of, to take her eyes from him. If his surveillance had been keen, hers was equally so, when she thought he wasn't looking. How could she tell this man where she lived? This was surely Poldary, the big house near the cliffs where Mr Manyard had lived? In the storm she hadn't been absolutely certain, but once in the kitchen she had known. How many times, as a child, had she sat here eating gingerbread men while her father had paid his rent and talked with his landlord?

Melissa had always come here with her father and old Mr Manyard had usually made a great fuss of her. Not always wisely, she realised. Hadn't he persuaded her father to send her to a better school than he could really afford and, after her father died, hadn't she, a few days later, run all the way here in order to beg Mr Manyard to make her mother let her stay on at the same school? She had been convinced Mr Manyard had only to speak and her mother wouldn't dare disobey. But that day she had been turned away from the door because, by some strange twist of fate, Mr Manyard, too, had died in his sleep and she was never to see him again.

Melissa had been fourteen, a very young fourteen at that. She had known nothing of Mr Manyard's will, nor had she tried to find anything out. The estate, she heard, had been left to a young man in his late twenties, a very distant cousin from New Zealand. To Melissa it seemed he must almost be as old as Mr Manyard! She had never seen the new owner, not until now. Of

course she couldn't be sure the man she was looking at
was he, but his whole demeanour seemed to suggest it.
His age too—she did a quick summing up; he looked
to be around thirty-five or six, which would just be
about right.

There had been other, more important, things to
divert Melissa at the time of his arrival. Her mother,
Mary Grant, had married again. When, during his
long illness, her father had been forced to hire extra
help on the farm, he had considered they were fortunate to find a man of some education who could
assist all round. Melissa still hated to think about it.
How, on the night before her father died, when quite
innocently she had gone to get a glass of milk she had
found her mother and this man embracing in the
kitchen.

Even at so young an age she had tried to convince
herself there was nothing so very awful about a man
and woman kissing each other, but she was horrified
when, two weeks after the funeral, her mother and
Lewis Cook married. She had been shocked, startled
almost out of her mind that her mother could have
done such a thing.

She could understand better now. Lewis Cook wasn't
a bad-looking man and her mother would never have
been much good at managing alone. It was the undue
haste, the clandestine meetings she hadn't been able
to forgive—this, and all the talk it had caused in the
district. And, as though the wedding couldn't have
been the culmination to a week of incredible happen-
ings, there had been worse to come. Cousin Helen
calling from the Midlands to present her gushing con-
dolences to a sorrowing widow, found instead a blushing bride.

Cousin Helen's husband had died some years before
and she had never chosen to replace him. She had been
as stunned as Melissa that Mary had married again so
soon. Melissa hadn't told her everything, but Helen was
family, her father's relation, someone she could turn

to. She felt more than a little ashamed now that she had sided so readily with Helen in the blazing row which had somehow sprung up between Helen and her mother but, at the time, she had only wanted to hurt her.

When Helen had offered her a home she had agreed immediately, being only too keen to get away from both Mary and the village. To her over-sensitive young ears the wagging tongues and curious faces were intolerable, not the nine days' wonder her mother said they would be. She didn't care that people would find something different to talk about next week, or that she had not, on occasion, been above a little gossiping herself. All she wanted was to escape.

Her mother, surprisingly enough, had raised few objections, her daughter's coldly condemning face not being the easiest of things to live with. Melissa realised now there had never been much sympathy between them. She had always been far more her father's daughter. Helen had no children of her own and plenty of money. She could do a lot for Melissa, she said. Eventually Mary gave permission for her to go for a year, but the year had stretched into six and in all that time Melissa had never once returned to Cornwall. Not until two weeks ago.

The man turned back to her, interrupting her thoughts abruptly. 'My name is Trevelyan, Ryan Trevelyan. What's yours?'

'Melissa Grant.' Blinking at such directness, she hazarded a guess that he would be none the wiser.

'Grant?' he frowned contemplatively. 'There aren't many Grants in the neighbourhood. Then you are a stranger?'

'You're the stranger, I believe, Mr Trevelyan.' She stared at him boldly in order to hide her dismay that he must be the new owner, as she had suspected.

He grinned mockingly, stepping nearer, his eyes again intent on her face. 'I should have thought not, not after six or seven years.'

She laughed at that, her eyes smouldering, her laughter deliberately taunting. 'Even ten times that number might not be enough for a man who chooses to act as you do!'

'Act as I do?'

Some of the wildness of the storm appeared to be invading her whole being, making her cry indiscreetly. 'You have threatened to put your tenants out on the street, Mr Trevelyan. Such a lack of consideration has little to recommend it.'

His eyes narrowed, as they met the dark blaze of her indignation with a quickness of mind that startled. 'Tenants? Ah, I see! So you're the daughter who deserted Mary Cook. I wondered why the name should ring a bell.'

'You sound as if you're thinking of rats and sinking ships, Mr Trevelyan!' she choked fiercely.

'It did occur,' he agreed smoothly, without noticeable remorse. 'I hadn't been here long when I was told of it. You left your mother when perhaps she needed you most. My memory is really quite phenomenal.'

'So it seems,' she jeered back at him, losing all sense of caution, as something about him seemed to dissolve all the hard-won discipline of years. 'You must remember, then, that my mother had another husband to comfort her?'

'While you felt entitled to any comfort that was going? Instead of feeling sorry for yourself, Miss Grant, you could have felt some compassion for your mother. Did you never think you might have driven her, even indirectly, to marry again?'

'What? By wanting to be away at school?'

'Maybe she felt unable to face an empty house, or unable to live in one, when you weren't there, with a man who wasn't her husband.'

Anger tore into Melissa along with his words. How dared he stand there condemning her? 'I should advise you never to judge without knowing the full facts, Mr Trevelyan.'

His eyes were cool on her white face. 'Which are?'

Suddenly she hung her head, an unusual action for her, but she couldn't tell him. It was something she had long put from her, refused to think about any longer. It was as if he had stabbed her with a knife, twisting it in the wound to cause the maximum of pain. Pain which struck her throat, making her feel sick, but still she couldn't tell him. Anyway, it would sound so ridiculous he would only laugh. She hadn't even told Helen in all the years she had lived with her.

'I asked you,' he insisted relentlessly, pushing her down into a chair by the fire, 'why you went. It might throw light on to several things which have puzzled me.'

'I can't think why.' She wished her arm would stop tingling each time he touched her. Nervously she wrenched free from his taut grip, uttering the first excuse she could think of. 'Maybe it was because—Lewis drank too much. He still does.'

'Yes,' Ryan Trevelyan didn't deny it, 'but I don't agree it's as bad as all that. I wouldn't complain if he made some effort to pay his rent. Not that this is something I would have mentioned if you hadn't brought it up.'

'You were asking the questions,' she reminded him coldly.

'No,' he corrected silkily, 'it was you who introduced the subject, after I introduced myself. Remember?'

Melissa flushed, more used to men who apologised even when she was in the wrong. 'I'll see what I can do when I get home,' she assured him stiffly, 'but surely to be a few months behind with the rent can't be considered a crime?'

'I think,' he said cynically, 'it's almost three years.'

'Three years!' Dismay clouded Melissa's green eyes and her mouth shook. 'How did this happen?'

'Didn't you have any idea?' he countered critically.

'No——' It was true, she had had no idea just how

bad things were. How could she when she had no contact whatsoever with her Cornish home? Melissa
watched the kettle boil, stared blindly while Ryan
Trevelyan reached for a teapot and began spooning
tea-leaves. It was frightening to think the sanctuary
she had sought could be in jeopardy. Not that she
would have come back if her own impulsiveness hadn't
brought her, but she couldn't return to Cousin Helen
now. Helen would never forgive her.

Melissa frowned, her smooth brow creasing anxiously
as she mentally surveyed the past six years. Helen had
given her a good home, an expensive schooling, done
everything she possibly could to alleviate Melissa's first
homesickness. Helen, with all her money, had been able
to supply more than enough of the good things in life
and Melissa had been grateful. After leaving school
she had willingly accompanied Helen on her trips
abroad, around the world, devoting herself almost entirely to looking after Helen's comfort. She'd never
dreamt that while she planned to repay Helen with a
lifetime of grateful servitude, Helen had been planning something entirely different, and it came as quite
a shock to learn that Helen had been secretly grooming
her for a successful marriage to the son of one of her
most affluent and influential friends.

Helen, herself, having married well, had the same
ambitions for Melissa. Long ago she had decided that
Melissa, with her stunningly elegant good looks, would
grace a title very well. Edward hadn't lived long
enough to acquire one himself, but she might easily
bask in Melissa's reflected glory. All this Melissa had
suddenly realised when it was nearly too late. She had
quite liked Freddy Taylor and grown used to having
him around, but she had objected with horror to his
hot, moist mouth and searching hands at the ball, two
weeks ago. Shouting at him, almost hysterically, she
had managed to free herself from his detaining arms
by pushing her hands hard across his leering, confi-
dent face. When he had announced smugly that Helen

agreed that Melissa should marry him, Melissa had panicked and flown.

At first she had absolutely refused to believe it, not until Helen had bluntly confirmed that he was speaking the truth. It seemed incredible that, in this century, there could still be arranged marriages, but Melissa was left in little doubt. Freddy Taylor was looking for the right kind of wife and Melissa would prove ideal. He also wanted her.

Cousin Helen's tone had brooked no disagreement. She had ruled Melissa for years and meant to continue doing so. 'His father has money, darling, more than he knows what to do with. Freddy is his only son and in love with you, what more could you want? And please don't accuse me of trying to run your life. You're so unworldly someone has to do it for you!'

Helen would never forgive her for running away, but it was all Melissa could think of. She had left notes for both her and Freddy, so they wouldn't be coming after her—at least she hoped not. She had only taken a few of her fabulous clothes—clothes which she now suspected she had been given in order to attract the right men. In coming back here she had, she supposed, burnt her boats completely and, somehow, she must try to live with the consequences of what many would call her own foolishness.

Rather apprehensively she watched Ryan Trevelyan pour the brewed tea. Leaving Helen's smart house hadn't been too difficult, just a matter of catching the right trains, but the exchanging of a rich environment for an extremely modest one was calling for more adjustment than she had ever thought possible. She wouldn't be telling the truth if she said there was nothing she missed. She even missed Helen, for all her duplicity. There was one person, however, whom she certainly didn't regret being without. That was Freddy Taylor, but, she acknowledged to herself, perhaps she wasn't being completely fair. When he had been willing to keep his distance she had liked him well enough.

He wasn't to know how she detested even the thought of being kissed.

The thick mugs which Ryan Trevelyan filled seemed to emphasise the difference between the life she had left and that of a farm—one so smooth, the other probably rough. As he passed her tea, studying her indifferently, she thought of another contrast. Ryan Trevelyan was somewhat different from other men of her acquaintance. He might admire her, but there was no warmth in the depth of his sombre gaze. There was a certain awareness but little appreciation. Hating all signs of male adulation as she did, she didn't know why the lack of it now should arouse a peculiar resentment.

'Drink that up,' he commanded, 'then I'll go and see what I can find for our supper.'

'Don't you have a housekeeper, Mr Trevelyan? I seem to remember my mother saying ...'

As Melissa's voice trailed off uncertainly, he smiled sardonically. 'I'm afraid my housekeeper is having a short break to attend a wedding. I'm on my own. At least I was.' With mockery his glance went over Melissa again.

Melissa, trying to stop herself imagining a kind of amused threat in his eyes, offered quickly, 'Perhaps I can help, then?' She didn't mention that she had never been allowed to do any cooking at Helen's, but surely it was only a matter of common sense? Anyway, anything was better than giving herself time to remember she was alone with this man and had no idea what he was really like.

Surprisingly he nodded; obviously the women he knew were fully competent in a kitchen. 'There's a dish of eggs over there and some ham. I wouldn't say no to an omelette.'

Swiftly she seized the excuse to prevent further discussion about the rent. If he was cold and hungry there could be better moments, if this was what he had in mind. An omelette should be easy.

Unfortunately it was not. She couldn't seem to remember how the ingredients should be mixed and grew impatient that she should feel so helpless. She hadn't a comb and her hair kept getting in the way, forcing her to ask if she might borrow one. While she dealt with her hair the omelette went so wrong it resembled leather.

He made a wry face at the first mouthful, pushing his plate aside insultingly. 'Cooking,' he observed sarcastically, 'is obviously not one of your accomplishments. I never knew a few eggs could be so ruined. That tastes burnt, and you seem to have used about a pound of salt.'

'Well, how was I to know you don't like your food well seasoned?' she snapped illogically, almost tearfully aware she couldn't eat her own portion either. 'I'll make coffee,' she offered sulkily, as with a sigh he began opening a tin of soup and cutting huge wedges of fresh bread.

While the soup and coffee heated she hunted around and found some cake in a tin in the large dresser. Cutting a sizeable chunk she placed it before him. 'There!' Secretly she hoped it would choke him.

'For a stranger,' he remarked idly, 'you believe in making yourself at home.'

'Do I have any choice?' she mumbled, her mouth full of her own piece of cake.

'Are you prepared to sing for your supper?' he asked suavely, his eyes wandering deliberately over her again.

She almost choked with indignation and fright—on a crumb! 'You—you're joking, of course?'

'The joke,' he retorted enigmatically, 'could be on me. You don't strike me as being a very grateful kind of girl, Melissa.'

She glared at his dry use of her name, her pulse still beating over rapidly. 'What sort of a girl do you think I am?' she challenged unwisely.

'If I answered frankly, you might think I was speaking of someone you didn't know,' he returned cryptically, making her suddenly flush for no reason she could think of. It was as if he knew something about her that she didn't. 'You aren't very practical,' he continued derisively. 'Scarcely able to cook an egg. What brings you back to these parts, I wonder? Not concern for your family, surely?'

'You don't make me sound a very nice character, Mr Trevelyan!' Quickly she jumped to her feet, full of a terrible kind of despair that he had assessed her so accurately. 'I'm sure you can't want any more of my company. If it's stopped snowing I can go now.'

'I wouldn't risk turning a cat out on a night like this.'

'Whatever category I come into, I'm going to try. My mother will be worrying.'

'You can ring.' His eyes held hers and she felt again the sudden flicker of awareness between them, a swift, deep quiver of heat which ran right down to her toes. She had neither the experience nor desire to dissect it, it only made her want to run.

'Yes,' she breathed quickly, 'I'm sure she'll know what to do.'

'The wires could be down.' He picked up the receiver and began to dial.

They weren't, but it was her stepfather who answered. 'You should have had more sense than to go out!' he grunted. 'Where are you?'

He seemed to have forgotten she had gone to collect some stores. 'Poldary,' she told him. 'Mr Trevelyan found me on the road. He isn't willing to take me any further tonight, but perhaps you would come for me?'

'Any reason why I should?' he shouted so loudly she knew Ryan Trevelyan must hear every word. 'After all, my dear, you've ignored your mother and me for six years. I'm certainly not going to commit suicide for you on a night like this!'

She tried to ignore his harsh tone. 'It's not very convenient for me to stay here. Mr Trevelyan's house-keeper is away.'

Lewis had always had a distorted sense of humour,

he gave her a taste of it now. He laughed harshly, 'Now's your chance to help your mother, then. You must owe her something.'

Apprehensively she gripped the receiver. Ryan Trevelyan turned, moving away, but she trusted his broad back no better than his cynical face. It seemed futile to lower her voice, but she did, asking cautiously, 'How could I help, right now?'

Lewis laughed again; she suspected he had been drinking. 'You're a good-looking girl, Melissa—do I have to spell it out? Whatever else he might not be, Ryan Trevelyan is certainly a man. He might be willing to overlook more than the rent if you slept with him.'

'How dare you!' Melissa cried, forgetting completely to lower her voice. 'I don't know a thing about Ryan Trevelyan, nor do I wish to, but I'm certainly not that kind of girl! If you didn't know before you know now.' Furiously she crashed down the receiver.

Raising her blank eyes from it at last, she saw Ryan Trevelyan watching sardonically from the other side of the table. 'It's quite an idea,' he grinned, 'but I might want more than one night. Even for one, however, I might be willing to consider it.'

Hatred choked her, almost. 'You listened!'

'Correction,' his eyes glinted, 'I simply put two and two together. I couldn't help overhearing some of it. You weren't exactly whispering, either of you.'

'It was Lewis's idea of a joke,' she mumbled, cheeks flaming.

'So I gathered.' He came around to where she sat, her hands still clenched, beside the telephone. Looking up, she saw herself reflected in the darkness of his speculative eyes. They seemed to pin her hypnotically so she couldn't look away. A flicker of something shot through her sharply and her legs went weak. Reaching for her shoulders, he took his time. 'I'm no hermit,' he said coolly.

Her green eyes widened with fascinated incredulity.

'But you don't even know me!'

'I've known you a couple of hours.'

'You mean——' disgust joined the other emotions racing across her expressive face, 'you mean you wouldn't mind having an affair with a stranger?'

He laughed, his head going back forcefully on his strong neck, his white teeth gleaming. 'Usually,' he admitted, 'I do try to get to know a girl first, but wouldn't you like to be the exception?'

CHAPTER TWO

'No!' Melissa jumped to her feet, quick fear galvanising her into action. She had never been in such a situation before, but pride caused her to lift her tenderly rounded chin even while terror raced through her. Surely a man in Ryan Trevelyan's position wouldn't do anything like this! 'You must believe I'm worth an awful lot?' she gasped.

'I think you might be,' he agreed shamelessly, his eyes narrowed on her flushed, indignant face. 'Mind you, I might be forced to reconsider in the morning.'

Her hand came up then to smack his face sharply. He didn't duck or try to stop her. It almost seemed there was something about her wild impetuousness he enjoyed. 'You're beastly!' she spluttered. 'I wouldn't sleep with you if you were the last man on earth. How dare you insult me! I'll have you know I could have been married now, if I'd wanted to be.'

If she had expected to shake him she was disappointed. 'Well, well,' he drawled, 'so someone was fool enough to offer you a ring? A bad-tempered, undisciplined little brat like you. Is this why you came running home? Didn't marriage and all its commitments appeal to you, or hadn't he enough money?'

Flinching from his tone, she wanted to do violence, but as her eyes met his, it was she who looked away first. 'I don't care about money,' she declared vehemently, 'and I'm not to be bought!'

'Don't tell me a girl like you would hold out for love?'

'I don't intend to marry. If I did fall in love—and I don't believe it really exists—I should ignore it. I hate being—touched.'

'You wouldn't,' he assured her, 'if you wanted someone badly enough.' His eyebrows rose mockingly. 'Of course I don't have to believe you. Maybe the lady protests too much?'

His hands came suddenly down on her slim shoulders, making her quiver, even as she tried to free herself. Was he seeking revenge in trying to frighten her by talking a lot of drivel? 'Take your hands off me!' she panted furiously.

'Not yet,' he murmured softly, lowering his head.

His wide, sensuous mouth was firm. Touching hers, it seemed to fuse every nerve in her body. There was nothing pleasurable in the flare of sharp sensation he aroused in her as his mouth crushed hers deliberately. Then, as molten fire leapt between them, his head lifted slightly, as if on a moment of surprised hesitation, before his lips came down ruthlessly again. Melissa found herself stunned, unable to move as his arms slid firmly around her, drawing her dazed body tightly against the muscled hardness of his, while his hand raked through her hair to angle her head so she couldn't escape him.

There was no way of avoiding the wild surge of primitive feeling that rushed through her, although she didn't recognise it as such—she was only aware of a peculiar desire to cling. Yet in the next second she was fighting madly, kicking and clawing him in terror as something beyond her control threatened to take over. 'Let me go, you beast! All men are horrible. Don't dare touch me again!'

'Steady!' His voice jerked her spinning senses to a standstill, as his hands caught her roughly before she could get completely away. 'It was merely a kiss. I wasn't going any further, not yet. Your comments on men I find interesting, if rather alarming.'

She wondered why, when his voice was so mocking, his eyes should be wary. Shaking off his hands, she backed against the wall like a small, caged animal. 'I told you I dislike being touched.'

He regarded her narrowly, not speaking for a full

minute. 'You could be playing hard to get,' he
shrugged, 'but I've had too busy a day to argue. Girls
seem to concentrate on finding new ways to arouse a
man's interest. I can hardly keep up. I'm not all that
desperate, though I confess you have me intrigued.'

Still staring at him, her face white, she unconsciously
rubbed her bruised mouth, as if desperate to remove
the imprint of his. She could find no comfort in his
odd assurances, mixed as they were with subtle threats,
nor in the way her heart was pounding, as if it had been
somehow cheated. 'I wish I could go home,' she whispered.

He shook his head adamantly. 'I'm afraid it's impossible,' he replied. 'I'm just wondering how I'm going to suggest showing you to your room so you won't
have hysterics. I'm not sure I have the patience to deal
with more of your childish tantrums, but I believe you
could do with your bed almost as much as I could,
after we've eaten.'

Next morning the wind blew warmly from the west
and the sun shone brightly through the clouds as he
drove her back home. The snow, surprisingly enough,
had began to thaw, but because the road was still partly
blocked he kept to the higher ground which ran along-
side it. Ryan Trevelyan appeared to know this part of
north-west Cornwall well, driving confidently but carefully, taking no risks. The darkness of Bodmin Moor
seemed to hold no fears for him and this morning,
gazing out over its snow-covered bleakness, Melissa
felt her old affection for it come rushing back.

She couldn't think why she should be seeing it
through new eyes after the almost sleepless night she
had spent, but she did. All her old love for the lonely
moors, the stark cliffs, the sheltered though sometimes
treacherous coves, seemed to renew itself and she felt
an odd relief. It came like a balm against the hate she
had known yesterday, the resentment she had felt at
having to return, and she couldn't help feeling that in
some mysterious way it had to do with the man sitting

beside her. This she tried to dismiss, but the conviction remained, for all his rough treatment of her. For all the anxious hours she had lain awake during the night in the large bedroom he had given her, consumed by fear and another indescribable emotion that he might decide to visit her. It hadn't been until daylight had crept tentatively through the window that she had realised her fears had been groundless.

They were almost there before he spoke. 'As some of the land I farm adjoins your mother's you'll probably be seeing something of me.'

'I see,' she replied coldly, keeping her face averted. 'Need I say I won't be looking!'

'That might not be sensible.' He treated her haughty tones with equal coldness. 'The least you can do is to be pleasant to your landlord.'

Melissa hung desperately on to her seat in order not to be thrown against him in the lurching vehicle. 'Is that a threat?'

Suddenly he was a grim stranger, not a deliberately taunting one as he had been last night but a cruel and dangerous man who chose not to be taken lightly. 'I've given your mother a few more weeks to get her affairs in order. I want to see you doing everything possible to help.'

'You want the place yourself?' she spat at him, quickly incensed that he should speak as if she was of no account. She felt mixed up, her moments of humiliation strangely at odds with the spoiling Helen had done over the past six years. Of course it hadn't been all spoiling, Melissa reflected bitterly, but she had been given a lot of her own way. In everything which hadn't mattered! Now her only defence seemed to lie in spitting out, and she was uncomfortably aware that Ryan Trevelyan knew it.

As they traversed a level stretch of ground he turned his head to glance at her shrewdly. 'No, I wouldn't want your land, but there are others who would be glad of it. A smallholding of good market garden soil along with a shop is something many would give their all for, and they'd be willing to devote themselves to it just as completely. I refuse to stand by and see it going to ruin much longer.'

What did he know of the rat race, she wondered scornfully, or the people caught in it? Wasn't he immune to such a way of life, secure in his riches? If she remembered correctly there were quite a few farms on his estate. Mr Ryan Trevelyan would know nothing about looking for pennies to pay rent! Nor would he bother himself in the least about a market garden and shop other than to calculate what he could make from it.

Any suggestion of friendship had disappeared by the time he dropped her off. 'I'll see what I can do,' she promised frigidly.

'You'd be advised to do that literally,' he bit out. 'Once you stooped to soil your pretty hands you might understand a lot of things better.'

She watched him turn with a grim change of gears, not caring for the contemptuous glance he threw at her. Her own expression was taut with a sullen dislike she didn't try to hide and she intentionally forgot to utter a word of thanks. As he already despised her it would make no difference. He probably wouldn't believe she was capable of feeling gratitude, anyway.

In the house she found her mother going through the morning mail. Her stepfather was still in bed.

'It's a miracle the post got through,' Mary Cook said, lifting her head from what looked suspiciously like a bill. She eyed Melissa curiously. 'The snow must have been worse up on the moors?'

'Yes.' Melissa reached for the teapot which was brewing on the stove, not because she particularly wanted a cup of tea, but it was something to do.

'Nice for you,' Mary commented dryly, looking much older than her fifty years, 'spending the night up at Poldary. I hope you made a good impression?'

Was her mother hinting at something? 'I was scarcely

there long enough to make any kind of impression, unless it was an unfavourable one. I don't think we took to each other—if you're talking about Ryan Trevelyan and me?'

'Oh, surely not?'

Melissa nodded, indifferently.

'Oh, you little fool!' Mary's face went pale, her eyes hardening. 'You had the chance. It seemed like fate that he should rescue you, and you such a good-looking girl. If you'd been blessed with brains, too, you should have had him eating out of your hand. He's not immune to a lovely woman, I've seen him with a few since he came here. You do know he's our landlord, Melissa?'

'Yes!' Melissa retorted, enraged and hurt that her mother could think this way. Just how far would she have expected her to go? The whole way by the sound of it. It seemed incredible that Mary should be willing to sacrifice even her only child in order to stave off disaster. The farm obviously meant much more to her than her daughter. 'I don't think Mr Trevelyan was greatly attracted,' she said quietly. 'I believe he's much more interested in the rent we owe him and I doubt if he would accept me instead. You do owe him money, Mum?'

'Yes,' Mary bit her lip. 'I find it very difficult to manage, you see. Your father——'

'He's not mine.'

Mary's cold face flushed. 'You've never forgiven me for marrying again, have you?'

'It doesn't matter. I'm sorry.' She could never tell her mother just what it was she couldn't forgive. It was too late to go into that now. Evasively she replied, 'You might have been wiser to have gone back to teaching when Dad died.'

Mary changed the subject fretfully. 'Well, I didn't, and if you won't help in any other way you could give me a hand here perhaps in the shop?'

'No,' Melissa shivered with distaste, 'I'm not going to slave there in order to provide Lewis with extra drinking money and—and waste my education. I'd rather not.'

'You mean you think you're too good now to stand behind a counter?' Mary challenged bitterly. Then, in more reconciliatory tones, 'It would only be for an hour or so, until I get lunch prepared and finished in the house.'

Eventually Melissa gave in, but with bad grace. Yet she didn't feel over-proud of her reluctance, nor of her silly outburst about wasting her education. She had left school more than two years ago and, though she liked doing something useful, she had never thought seriously of a possible career. Being at Helen's beck and call had, she supposed, been almost a full-time job even if she'd never thought of it that way.

'If you would just see to the newspapers,' Mary called after her as she went out, 'I won't be long.'

Running up to her room, Melissa quickly washed her hands and face before going across the yard to the shop. Unlocking the door, she opened the old-fashioned shutters, frowning as she looked around the cluttered interior. It was fairly clean but very untidy with boxes of vegetables all over the place instead of in orderly rows. As it was primarily a market garden shop they also sold garden utensils and packets of seed. Melissa saw these had simply been left in rough piles while the proper racks provided were standing empty. How different, she recalled, from her father's day when everything had been kept in spick and span order.

As there was no other shop in the small village they supplied the local newspapers and cigarettes along with sweets. Mary said these didn't pay very much, but they did bring in customers who often bought something else. Today the newspapers were late in arriving and, as she waited for them, Melissa managed to sell one of the farmers' wives some gardening gloves, ready for the finer weather which the woman prophesied was coming with spring.

She had just gone, saying her husband would pick up the newspaper later, when Ryan Trevelyan walked in. Melissa felt so dismayed she wanted to sink through the floor. He was the last person she had expected to see. How he must be laughing, behind that expressionless mask, to have caught her in such a humiliating position!

'My paper, please?' He fished in his pocket for change while she stared at him blankly.

'I beg your pardon?'

'My paper,' he repeated, regarding her bewildered face with mild irritation. 'I get one every day. It's ordered.'

'Wouldn't it be easier to have it sent by post?' she asked foolishly, the thought of having him calling each morning being more than she could seem to bear.

'Perhaps,' he watched her pink cheeks with interest, 'but I never got round to arranging it and, where your mother is concerned, every little must help.'

'Well, they haven't arrived yet, I'm afraid.' Melissa turned away, hoping he would take the hint and come back later, when she wasn't here. Even to be near him affected her adversely. Something bubbled up inside her, making her heart beat so she felt completely shaken. Silently she blamed it on the brutal way he had kissed her, and she decided she must get rid of him, even if it meant being rude.

She might have known his skin was of the thicker variety. He settled his long length on the edge of one of the lower counters. 'I'm sure they'll not be long. I'll wait.'

'You could wait all day,' she suggested desperately, 'in this weather. Surely you're too busy to—to hang around here.'

'You do have a nice turn of phrase, Miss Grant,' he laughed, 'but you must remember the customer is always right. I'll hang around, as you so elegantly put it, for a little while. It will save me coming back.'

'Just as you like,' she replied stiffly, her face like ice.

He eased his weight on the counter, staring at her closely, not apparently disturbed by her smouldering green eyes. 'So you've decided to help at last?'

She swung around to him on a deep breath. 'Really, Mr Trevelyan, what I do is my own business!'

'Not in this case it isn't.' His dark brows rose derisively, 'When my rent isn't being paid I must have the right to object to idle hangers-on.'

'I don't care whether you get your rent or not!' she hissed defiantly, wading in regardless of his calculating expression. 'For anyone else I might have been prepared to work my fingers to the bone, but not you! I'm only here for an hour until Mum finishes in the house.'

'And then?' His voice was so quiet she was lulled into imagining she had won this round at least.

'Oh,' she said carelessly, 'I might go somewhere and amuse myself for the rest of the day, if the road clears and I can get the car out.' She had no intention of going anywhere, but he needn't know this.

To her surprise he didn't lose his temper. If she provoked him, as she half hoped she did, he gave no indication. He merely shrugged, although she suspected by the slight tightening of his mouth that he curbed more violent impulses.

He said coolly, changing the subject so suddenly she felt startled, 'I'm holding a party next week, for charity. I hope you and your parents will be able to come.'

A party. She hated to think of the last one she'd been to. Meeting his bland gaze hastily, she looked as quickly away again. 'I'm not in the mood for parties just now, I'm afraid. Besides, as you must know, Lewis might only get drunk, and this would upset Mum.'

'I'm sure I could cope with Lewis's tendency to imbibe too much,' he rejoined smoothly. 'If they refuse you can always come yourself, seeing how you like to get around.'

'No, thank you.'

'I'm sure you'll change your mind, Melissa, when you've had time to think it over.' He paused as if he wanted every word to sink in. 'I believe you'd be wiser to accept.'

'It was like a threat,' Melissa said later to Mary, 'but of course I'm not going.'

Mary looked wistful. 'At one time we were invited everywhere.'

'You know why you aren't now!' Melissa retorted cynically.

'Lewis isn't as bad as all that!' Mary protested. 'It's not so much that we aren't asked, there's just nothing to spare for clothes, I'm afraid. We went out to supper a few weeks ago. June Heron asked us.'

Melissa crinkled her brow. 'Wasn't she the girl you went to college with?'

Mary nodded, dismissing her friend abstractedly. 'Did you say Ryan Trevelyan came himself for his morning paper?'

'Yes, and to issue his invitation,' Melissa sniffed. 'It sounded more like a royal command, and I'm not going, as I've already told him.'

Lewis came in from the gardens and joined in the argument, supporting Mary, and more. 'You wouldn't want to see your mother thrown out of her house, would you? We had Cousin Helen on the line last night and she was saying how you could have helped us by marrying a certain Mr Taylor. It seems you've put your foot in things there, however, and it appears you're about to do the same thing again.'

Trying to ignore his peevish sarcasm, Melissa said bleakly, 'It was nice of Helen to ring, but I'm afraid I'm not going to marry Freddy Taylor.'

'You could try doing something,' he sighed.

Melissa sighed too, but tensely. Why did everyone seem to think she could solve her mother's problems? Ryan Trevelyan had pointed out that she could work harder, while Lewis had decided she could marry money! 'You forget I was in the shop this morning before you were up, Lewis. You can't say I'm not trying!'

'You could do better in other ways,' he said cryptically.

Not by selling myself to a man, Melissa vowed furiously, as she set off later to rescue the stranded car from
the moors. It was the middle of the afternoon and the
snow-blower had just come down and told them the
road was clear. Mary wanted the supplies she had
brought from Bude which were still in the boot of the
car. Someone from the village gave her a lift to where
she had left it, but she was startled to find it was gone.

The friendly neighbour advised her to get in touch
with the police, but she hesitated. There were tire
marks over the snow; it could be that Mr Trevelyan
had been busy. 'I'll ask my mother first,' she hedged,
waving the man goodbye.

As soon as he was out of sight she made across the
moor towards Poldary. It was easy enough to follow
the tracks. The car looked as though it had been towed
by a tractor. Why should Ryan Trevelyan have taken
it there? Now everyone must know where she'd spent
the night, and if this was his idea of a joke she didn't
appreciate his sense of humour!

Most of the snow had gone, but the sudden thaw
made the ground very wet and slippery. Melissa was
breathless by the time she reached the house and quite
out of temper. She could see no sign of the car and, as
she gazed blankly around the empty yard, she felt
slightly sick with worry. Not being nearly so indifferent
to her mother's plight as she pretended to be, she realised that to lose the only form of transport they had
might prove the final disaster.

She knocked loudly on the back door which eventually opened to disclose a woman Melissa took to be the
housekeeper, as she wore a large white apron over her
overall, which seemed to suggest she was busy preparing the evening meal. She was middle-aged and craggy,
very severe-looking, and stood staring at Melissa coldly.

'Yes?' she said sharply.

'I—Is Mr Trevelyan at home, please?' Melissa felt

impatient with herself for faltering so, but the woman
was somehow intimidating. 'I expect,' she rushed on in
confusion, 'you're his housekeeper?'

'I am!' The woman drew herself up, her aggressive
manner indicating she was not to be treated lightly,
especially by a girl as shabby as Melissa. 'I'm Mrs Barr.'

How Melissa wished she had been facing Mr Manyard's old housekeeper, who had been warm and
friendly and fed her with gingerbread men. She, apparently, had gone. Melissa wondered where. 'How
do you do,' she held out her hand politely to this latest
paragon, 'I'm Melissa Grant.'

Mrs Barr ignored the hand, merely nodding slightly.

Melissa sighed and tried again. 'I asked about Mr
Trevelyan?'

'I'm afraid he's engaged at the minute,' Mrs Barr replied primly. 'I wouldn't care to interrupt him.'

'Oh,' Melissa was nonplussed. What did she do now?
Impulsively she explained, 'I just wondered if he knew
anything about my car. It broke down last night on the
moor road.'

'Ah!' Mrs Barr's eyes glittered even more coldly. 'So
you would be the one who spent the night in Mr Trevelyan's bed!'

The way Mrs Barr said it implied something quite
improper, which simply wasn't true. Melissa's cheeks
flushed scarlet, which she realised furiously must make
her look extremely guilty. 'I'm sure you're mistaken,'
she gasped.

Digging in her voluminous pocket, Mrs Barr drew
forth a hair-slide, a large one with a catch that Melissa
immediately recognised.

'Is this yours?' Mrs Barr asked, and, when Melissa
nodded, passed it to her. 'I'm glad you didn't try to
deny it. I found it on the floor in Mr Trevelyan's room
this morning. Besides, I knew at once his bed was quite
different from usual.'

Horrified, Melissa stared at Mrs Barr's disapproving
face. The slide must have dropped from her pocket.

She had a habit of pushing it into the back pocket of her jeans in case she should need it; it must have fallen out. If she hadn't been in such a hurry this morning she might have noticed. How could Ryan Trevelyan have given her his room? Hadn't he been aware Mrs Barr might find out? It had been bad enough having to stay with him alone last night, but nothing had happened apart from that one kiss, which couldn't be construed as anything like what she supposed Mrs Barr had in mind. Melissa gulped. Hadn't she risen early, this morning, in order to get away before anyone could discover she had been here? She did remember Ryan saying something about no other room being properly aired, but she never imagined he had given her his.

Still, she wasn't going to try explaining or making excuses to Mrs Barr. Judging from the lady's expression she had already been tried and condemned! 'Mr Trevelyan was very kind in giving up his room,' she answered coolly, 'but we didn't share it. Now could you please ask him if he would see me for a moment? I won't keep him long.'

Such deceptive composure appeared to confuse Mrs Barr, who nodded uncertainly. 'If you'll just wait here, miss, I'll see what I can do.'

She was back surprisingly quickly, looking faintly put out. 'Mr Trevelyan has agreed to see you.' Her voice stiffened as she added rather smugly, 'I'm afraid he's entertaining a lady friend but will spare you a minute.'

So this was the reason for Mrs Barr's sudden capitulation, Melissa reflected wryly as she followed her inside. She meant to show Melissa she was of little consequence in Ryan Trevelyan's life. Melissa was to be shown this special girl-friend which should be enough to put an end to any foolish notions she might be entertaining about Mr Trevelyan! If it hadn't been so ridiculous Melissa might have laughed. Why, she hadn't known him more than twenty-four hours. They were almost strangers.

Aware of this, she felt confused that her heart should beat faster when Mrs Barr opened the study door and her eyes met his. He was standing, one arm casually along the mantelpiece, smiling lazily down at the girl sitting on a small sofa before the fire, but when he raised his head to glance at Melissa his smile faded.

Melissa's eyes widened as she took in the cosy scene. A tea tray stood on a low table by the hearth and there was a delicious smell of toasted crumpets. The girl, who Melissa guessed was some years older than herself, was busy pouring tea and had the air of someone well established.

'You asked to see me, Melissa?' Ryan Trevelyan enquired, and she heard Mrs Barr's faintly scandalised breath as she abruptly closed the door. By calling her Melissa so familiarly, he had no doubt confirmed Mrs Barr's suspicions that whatever had gone on here last night had been far from innocent!

'It's about the car,' Melissa said hastily, her cheeks flushing with anger as she was suddenly convinced Ryan was quite aware of what Mrs Barr was thinking. 'It's gone from the road and I followed its tracks to Poldary.'

'Ah yes, your car.' His mouth tightened as he surveyed her resentful face. Then, as if it had only just occurred to him, 'You won't have met Miss Angela Brett?'

As Melissa shook her head, Miss Brett smiled distantly but made no attempt to shake hands as Ryan introduced them. She said coolly, 'You must be the daughter of the woman who runs that quaint little shop in the village?' Her thin brows rose and her expression as her eyes went over Melissa was disparaging. 'Isn't the smallholding on your estate, Ryan darling?'

'Yes,' he nodded briefly, his eyes returning to Melissa, boring into her before slipping to her mouth, almost as if he wished they had been alone. Yet he made no attempt to offer her a cup of tea, or even a chair, but kept her standing as if agreeing with Miss Brett's obvious opinion that she was of little consequence!

'Your car, Melissa,' he went on, 'is in the local garage. I've asked them to make sure it's completely roadworthy before letting you have it again. I've also told them to send me the bill.'

'But why?' Melissa's voice rose in sheer fright. 'It only needed a change of tire!'

'Your spare was flat too.'

'Oh,' she gulped, 'I didn't notice.' Trust Lewis, she thought, not to, either! 'But that's no reason for sending it to the garage!'

'Didn't you realise the car's over ten years old and not fit to drive in its present condition?'

'I'm sure it's not as bad as all that!' she cried indignantly, hating his superior tones almost as much as Miss Brett's silent amusement. 'I think you went much too far, sending it to the garage without consulting me.'

She glared at him and he looked steadily back until Angela Brett's cool laughter came between them.

'Perhaps she's right, Ryan darling. I shouldn't have bothered if I'd been you and you'll obviously get no thanks for paying the bill. You should get your mother to buy you a new car, Miss Grant. My parents gave me a beauty for my last birthday.'

'Perhaps she will.' Melissa swallowed as she lifted her chin. Miss Brett must know perfectly well Mary hadn't that kind of money.

'They can't afford it.' Ryan spoke so derisively Melissa could have hit him. Did he have to proclaim to all and sundry that they were broke? Or was he merely warning her against asking for one? It hurt, somehow, that he might imagine she would. As for the car—she knew quite well it wasn't in a good condition, but what could they do about that?

'Mum only uses the car for delivering orders,' she said coldly. 'It doesn't take a brand new machine for that.'

'I'll let you have something until it's fixed,' Ryan replied, as if she was wasting her time trying to make him change his mind. His mouth curled at the corners as he watched her and she was sure it wasn't in amusement. 'I'm sorry if it's put an end to your little jaunt. Didn't you say you might be going into town this afternoon, Melissa? You'll just have to find a nice benevolent friend to drive you there.'

'When I need your advice I'll ask for it!' Melissa cried, momentarily forgetting the observant Miss Brett as she wondered how he could so easily reduce her to such childish utterances. 'If I contact the garage immediately they might not have started on the repairs.'

'They already have.' His eyes impaled hers coolly. 'I forgot to mention it this morning. Once it's been repaired and passed its M.O.T. you can collect it, but not a moment sooner. Now, if you don't mind, I'll ring for Mrs Barr to show you out.'

Her cheeks a dull red, this time with smouldering humiliation, Melissa rejected his offer bitterly. 'Thank you, I can see myself out!'

'Good idea,' he rejoined sardonically. 'Mrs Barr has really enough to do.' As if dismissing her out of hand, he turned to smile down again at the simpering Angela, leaving Melissa to almost run from the room.

The most difficult part was having to tell Mary and Lewis what had happened to the car. She also felt forced to confess that Ryan Trevelyan had said he would pay for it.

'We can't let him, of course,' she insisted. 'It would only put us deeper in his debt.'

'I'll have to owe him, then,' Mary sighed wistfully. 'I expect you're right. It wouldn't be the thing to allow him to pay.'

'Why not?' Lewis was dressed to go out with some of his friends. 'It looks as if he's taken quite a fancy to our pretty daughter, Mary, and if he's willing to pay for the privilege of knowing her, that's up to him.'

'It has nothing to do with me,' Melissa said sharply, hurt that they should both seem so willing to take the easy way out. 'Must you make everything so personal and sordid, Lewis? I told him we wouldn't take his money. As for the other, I don't think he even likes me very much.'

Lewis retorted blandly, a sarcastic smile on his still fairly good-looking face, 'Let me tell you something, my girl. Ryan Trevelyan doesn't make a habit of paying other people's bills, but I have heard that when he wants something he doesn't let anything stand in his way. In this case it could either be you or this small-holding, but whichever it is, I have little doubt he'll get it in the end.'

'Well, it won't be me!' Melissa informed him, impulsively. 'He was entertaining a girl to tea, a Miss Brett, and they seemed very friendly.'

'Angela's been around a long time,' Mary nodded. 'The housekeeper did once tell me she thought they might get married eventually.'

'So you see, Lewis,' Melissa wondered why her voice should sound despondent rather than triumphant, 'you're quite wrong, regarding me anyway.'

Lewis clearly wasn't impressed, but he only replied, 'Time will tell,' in his most portentous manner, as he went out.

Next morning Melissa was in the shop when Ryan came for his newspaper. Mary was suffering from a sick headache and Melissa had advised her to go back to bed. She had completely forgotten about the shop. When Mary had feebly asked about it, Melissa had been left with no alternative but to offer to open it again.

Trying to convince herself she hated it, she found she could no longer ignore the general clutter which rendered it almost impossible to move. She was attempting to tidy up when Ryan strode in.

He smiled slowly at the sight of her struggling with a bag of potatoes, her slight form, in her old jeans, bent almost double. 'I see you're still trying?'

As he made no effort to help, she stopped what she was doing and sat on one of the neat paper sacks, eyeing him coldly. Then remembering he would be here for his morning paper, not to torment her, she jumped to her feet again and, rushing across to the counter, lifted one from the pile and thrust it at him.

'Eight pence, please.' She thought it would be more dignified to ignore what he said. Instead she allowed her glance to roam blankly over him, as if she couldn't care less what he thought. Yet her heart shuddered queerly. This morning he looked almost as shabby as she in a pair of well worn cords and an old tweed jacket, but whatever he wore never seemed to detract from the impact of his hard, masculine figure.

Suddenly, as he appeared in no great hurry to find the right change, she recalled something she wanted to speak to him about, something she had found impossible to mention in front of Angela Brett. 'Why did you let me sleep in your room when I was forced to stay in your house?'

'Ah, that——' he drawled idly, his voice so toneless she suspected him of mocking, 'It seems so long ago.'

Her suspicions confirmed as she met his glinting eyes, she exclaimed sharply, 'Mr Trevelyan, I asked you a question!'

CHAPTER THREE

As Melissa stood staring at him his brows rose at her obvious resentment. 'Don't tell me my good deed wasn't appreciated?'

Melissa's green eyes smouldered. 'I believe you did it deliberately, out of a perverted sense of humour!'

'Maybe.' He drew nearer, his glance scanning her face with an intent satisfaction as if looking for flaws and finding none. 'It was the only one properly aired and I distinctly remember mentioning it.'

She shrank from his penetrating surveyal, as she had done before, yet her whole body seemed alight with a kind of blind fury which made her persist. 'But you gave no clear indication that the room was yours, and you do have central heating!'

'Which Mrs Barr, in the name of economy, usually keeps switched off in the bedrooms not in use.'

'You could have turned it on.'

'I could, and I did,' his voice deepened with impatience, 'but you might have been frozen before it made any difference to the temperature. Better to concentrate on the sacrifice I made rather than your silly imagination.'

Which only made it worse! 'I can't imagine you freezing to death!' she cried angrily.

He appeared to restrain himself with an effort. 'Fortunately I didn't turn in until after midnight.'

'You said you were tired?'

'Yes—well,' he rubbed his jutting chin thoughtfully as he watched her flushed face, 'perhaps I wasn't tired enough. I decided to write a few letters. I have business interests in New Zealand, and relatives, with whom I have to keep in touch.'

'Why don't you go back there?' Melissa suggested sullenly. 'You must know that strangers are never really accepted in these parts.'

He laughed infuriatingly. 'Come, Miss Grant, we aren't still living in the Dark Ages. People around here appear to like me well enough. Don't you think you should stop trying to vent your temper on me, just because you were fool enough to leave something lying on my bedroom floor? If it's any consolation, Mrs Barr is no gossip.'

That's all you know, Melissa wanted to cry, while knowing she couldn't. She had no proof that Mrs Barr had told anyone where she had spent the night, but she had an uneasy feeling Mrs Barr wasn't as discreet as Ryan Trevelyan thought! If this was what he really thought? He always sounded so smooth, so glib, with a too ready answer to everything, a too decisive determination to be master of every situation. Combined with his dangerous masculinity it seemed to turn him into the kind of man she had never before known.

'Listen, Miss Grant.' He had her by the shoulders before she could move away. 'I'd rather you didn't look at me as if I'd committed the sin of the year. I didn't dream up that storm, or a vision by the roadside. I didn't even know you were a girl until we got back to Poldary. No one else might have found you, and I don't think I exaggerate in saying you probably owe me your life.'

No, never that! Melissa shrank from both the man and the truth, as his grip seemed to burn through her thin sweater to her tender skin. She couldn't bear to owe him anything, especially when the glint in his eyes proclaimed he didn't intend she should forget it! 'A night's shelter could be a high price to pay for a ruined reputation,' she said tightly. 'The thaw soon set in.'

'You seem to imply,' he taunted, 'that I could have arranged it sooner. The thaw didn't arrive until almost daylight, although it had stopped snowing. You could have tried walking back to the village, but you might have been frozen to death. We both know that on the moors it has happened.'

Her lips curled and her chin lifted in angry disdain. 'You can't expect me to feel indebted to you!'

He jerked her nearer, his face inches from her hot one. 'I never do anything for nothing,' he ground out, 'not unless it suits me and, in your case, it definitely doesn't. But, as far as repayment goes, you can take your time. I wouldn't want you to think about it until you're good and ready.'

Beneath his hands she suddenly trembled, not quite getting his meaning, only the clear impression that he wouldn't wait for ever. 'You'll never get anything from me!'

'I shouldn't bet on it,' his breath fanned her cheek, 'but that's for the future. Meanwhile, if you continue to accuse me of damaging your reputation I might forget you dislike being—pawed, and give you something to really worry about!'

Wildly Melissa struggled to free herself, panic rising sharply within her as she wondered what he meant to do next. He might have come from New Zealand but, as he held her, there seemed so much of the darkly forbidding Cornishman in him that she trembled. His words could mean so much or very little. He would never give her the satisfaction of explaining them exactly. Possibly he intended she should live in fear while his threats were actually empty?

She need not have been frightened. With a contemptuous thrust, almost as if he could read the shuddering slimness of her body exactly, he pushed her down again on to the sack of potatoes. From his pocket he took eight pence and, before her widening gaze, dropped it in her lap. 'I'd better not stop you working, while you're in the mood. I'll see you later.'

Melissa hoped frantically she wouldn't see him for a very long time, but she might have known it was too much to hope for. That evening, after dinner, as they were drinking coffee around the comfortable lounge fire, the doorbell rang. Lewis made no attempt to do anything about it and when Mary began struggling to her feet Melissa jumped up and said she would answer it. When she opened the door it was Ryan.

'I'd like to see your mother,' he requested coolly, as Melissa stood silently staring at him. 'It's a small matter of business which has cropped up. Someone asked me to give it my immediate attention and I'm afraid I forgot about it until I bumped into him a short while ago.'

'I see.' Unable to steady her jumping nerves, Melissa spoke tartly. 'I was beginning to think you were the local ghost.'

'I'm a bit too substantial, am I not?' he grinned. 'And if I do seem to be haunting you, it's probably just a trick of your imagination. You could be flattering yourself, Miss Grant.'

'Possibly,' she snapped, as Mary came through to see who was calling.

'Melissa!' she cried reproachfully, 'why haven't you invited Mr Trevelyan in? My daughter,' she added apologetically, throwing Melissa a dark glance, 'isn't usually so lacking in manners.'

Not waiting to be asked twice, Ryan strode into the hall, carrying Melissa with him. Her breath did strange things in her throat as she felt his hard, lean fingers curling around her arm. She was his prisoner and, unless she made a scene, she couldn't escape.

'Do come this way, Mr Trevelyan.' Mary led them into the lounge and Melissa felt suddenly thankful, for the first time, that it was a large, extremely well furnished room. It might be rather shabby and not in quite the same class as Poldary, but it was very nice. Her real father, she remembered, had spent a lot of money on it, in order to please his wife. For a brief moment Melissa's eyes rested on Mary bitterly.

Mary, smiling warmly, motioned for Ryan to sit down. He did, seemingly quite at ease, taking Melissa with him on to the chintz-covered settee, his fingers still locked on her arm as if he had intentionally forgotten about them. Melissa noticed that Lewis, for all his weaknesses, appeared to have retained the basic courtesies. He rose to his feet when Ryan came in and, after greeting him politely, asked what he would have to drink.

Once settled, Ryan did relax his excruciating hold and Melissa moved furtively along the settee away from him. Yet for all she tried to prevent it, her gaze kept wandering back to him, until almost disgusted at her own sensuous response to the long length of his powerful body, she stared fixedly into the fire. She heard him reply to Lewis that he would rather join them for coffee, if there was any left, as he had just had a drink at Tom Brown's place.

'You are having a busy evening,' Melissa observed spitefully, hoping to relieve some of her taut feelings as her mother rushed to find another cup with what Melissa considered undue haste. Did she have to treat Ryan Trevelyan like royalty! Tom Brown, she recalled, was a neighbour. He would also be one of Ryan's tenants. One who managed to pay his rent, no doubt!

Lewis resumed his seat and Ryan, ignoring her little taunt, began talking casually about country matters. She wasn't really surprised that Lewis could sound very knowledgeable when he chose. He had, she knew, a degree in agriculture and that his family were fairly well-to-do, but unfortunately Lewis had quarrelled with them. They had thrown him out and he had never gone back. Mary had told her, only a few days ago, that he had recently approached his now elderly parents for a loan, but without success. They hadn't, she had added bitterly, even been pleased to hear from him after all this time and, as he was the younger of two sons, it seemed unlikely he would inherit anything.

Finishing his second cup of coffee, Ryan glanced from Lewis to Mary, encompassing them both. 'It's the field at the top of your holding I've come to see you about. Tom Brown would like it and, as you don't appear to be using it, I wondered if you would be willing to let him have it. Naturally your rent would be adjusted accordingly.'

'The top field? Oh, no!' Melissa gasped before anyone could speak. 'Oh, Mum—you can't let him have that! I always kept my pony there, and it's very good pasture.'

'But you don't have a pony now, Melissa. You'd be too old for one, anyway.' Mary spoke sharply.

'Even if I wasn't I suppose we couldn't afford one,' Melissa retorted bleakly. She didn't look at Ryan, but hated him fiercely for deliberately trying to take their land away. He must realise how little they had, and although Melissa had left it six years ago she was still fond of the small farm—all of it!

'I could always let you have a horse to ride at Poldary,' Ryan offered surprisingly, as Mary sighed impatiently. 'I have several and they don't always get enough exercise.'

Melissa's lip curled. She wouldn't stoop to even think about such an offer, at least not from him! 'Wouldn't Miss Brett help out?' she jeered, remembering the girl's obvious devotion.

'Unfortunately she's usually too busy.'

Melissa shrugged indifferently, mistrusting Ryan's even tones. She considered it doubtful that Angela Brett would be too busy for anything Ryan Trevelyan might suggest. 'I'd still rather have a horse of my own,' she replied, mentioning, without thinking, 'I've been used to having one at Cousin Helen's.'

'But you can't have one here. I mean, Melissa,' her mother paused in embarrassment, her eyes flickering from Ryan's cold, hard face to her daughter's stubborn one, 'we can't afford it,' she said flatly.

Ryan glanced at Melissa, as if he would liked to have put her over his knee and dealt with her without further words, but a moment later his face was wiped clean of its harsh expression. Suddenly he rose to his feet. 'If Melissa wants the field we'll let her have it.

I'll tell Tom Brown there's nothing doing, unless she changes her mind. Now, perhaps, she'll see me out?'

He thanked Mary quietly for the coffee, nodding briefly to Lewis and, because Mary seemed weakly disinclined to move, Melissa was left with no alternative but to do as he asked.

Feeling strangely uneasy, she followed him through the lounge door. Discussion about the field had scarcely got started. Why was he leaving so abruptly in the middle of it? He must know that the final decision wouldn't have rested with her, and, owing him as much as they did, both Lewis and Mary might have been perfectly willing to let Tom Brown have the field. Melissa bit her lip. She enjoyed riding, but she didn't mind all that much about not having a horse. Uncertainly she glanced at him. Maybe he enjoyed making her feel ashamed of herself!

He surprised her still further by saying smoothly, 'Since you don't want to come to Poldary I might supply a horse to go in the field you're so keen on keeping.'

'You don't have to be that generous,' Melissa smiled coolly, her remorse quickly forgotten beneath the overwhelming suspicion that he had no intention whatsoever of letting her keep the wretched field. 'I'm afraid I don't accept such favours from strangers.'

'But I'm not just any man, am I, Melissa?' He halted in the shadowed hall which the low-watt bulb lit only dimly. His eyes, as he looked down at her, were narrowed to slits of ice. 'Find yourself a coat. We'll go and have a drink somewhere while you consider my offer.'

'No, thank you!' she retorted breathlessly, shrinking away from him, exclaiming wildly, 'The less I accept from you the better.'

'The more you object the longer I'm going to have to spend persuading you, and I'm not in the mood to cajole or waste time, Melissa.'

His strength, being of the mind as well as physical, made her shiver with distaste. He had every appearance of a man used to getting everything he wanted, but whatever he wanted of her she must make sure he didn't get! Nor must she, for one moment, consider taking anything. 'If you're tired you don't need me,' she persisted.

'Maybe you're right,' he rejoined darkly. 'I don't personally have much use for spoilt little girls who can scarcely boil an egg, but perhaps Poldary does, and the sooner we get to know each other the better.'

'But why?'

Suddenly he was extremely non-committal. 'Possibly I'm still curious about you.'

'Well, I'm not about you!'

He said, between his teeth, 'Get your coat. Unless you want me to drag you along as you are!'

She shivered against his leashed anger, but had been used to having her own way too long not to be obstinate. Besides, she felt too wary of him, of the vivid fear and unpredictable longing he induced. Her dazed mind had to grope for the next objection. 'I'm not dressed.'

His eyes glinted over her. 'If you mean you aren't wearing something smart, it doesn't matter. We aren't going to that kind of place.'

Somehow Mary's weary face came between Melissa and another refusal. With a shrug which was anything but gracious she snatched her jacket from a peg while Ryan returned to the sitting room and told them they were going out.

'I don't wish to go far,' Melissa muttered, as she sat beside him in his car, which was a far cry from the one Mary owned.

'You'll go as far as I wish before I'm done with you,' he retorted, low-voiced, as if still angry. Then, more mildly, 'Don't worry, we'll find some quiet little pub for an hour. If you could bring yourself to relax you'd feel better.'

'Not with you,' she flashed him a defiant glance. 'No girl likes being ordered around, and if my company is supposed to compensate for the non-payment of rent then I hope you won't be too disappointed.'

'You must make sure that I'm not,' he said smoothly.

Melissa choked with temper and revulsion. 'You may consider me spoilt, able to think of no one but myself, but it's only for my mother's sake that I'm with you now.'

His mouth twisted dryly and it was clear he didn't believe her. 'You came because I didn't leave you any other option. You don't have to pretend a consideration for others which you don't possess. Now sit back. I told you before, my objective tonight is merely to satisfy my curiosity, that's all.'

With a great effort Melissa bit back a too ready retort and subsided miserably. So he was curious. She knew what that meant. He would want to know what sort of life she had lived with Helen, why she hadn't a career, why she wasn't married. She had heard it all before, chiefly from men Helen and she had met on their travels. As with them, it would be useless to tell him she had grown tired of pursuing such an idle existence like that. Helen had given her a lot, just as long as Melissa had always been there, at her beck and call. Yes, Ryan Trevelyan, like the others, would ask, but she was used to parrying too impertinent queries. He could probe and bully as much as he liked, but he wouldn't be getting any straight answers!

The pub he took her to was large and obviously popular, although it wasn't so much crowded as comfortably full. With his hand firmly at her elbow he marched her swiftly through the bar, pausing only to leave an order.

'Oh, good evening, Mr Trevelyan,' the landlord nodded, his greeting cordial, before returning to the customer he was attending to. Suddenly his glance shot back, widening appreciatively on Melissa. 'What can I get you, Mr Trevelyan?' He shovelled change into his till, his eyes not once leaving Melissa's face.

Ryan asked for two beers. He didn't ask Melissa what she would like and her resentment showed in the stiffness of her slender back as he guided her to a seat at the far end of the lounge. 'It won't do you any harm,' he said mildly, as they were served. 'Who knows, our landlord might have put ambrosia in yours. He seems quite taken.'

Melissa, who was used to interested male glances, merely shrugged.

'It's nothing new to you, is it?' Ryan's own eyes, far from reflecting admiration, flicked her derisively, with something in their depth she couldn't properly define. 'Even in a pair of disreputable old jeans you stand out from every other woman in the room. A combination of good looks and sex appeal.'

He certainly didn't pull his punches! As for the latter, with his six foot two of smoothly muscled frame, he had more than enough himself. The blonde in the corner was watching him surreptitiously. If only he wasn't so adept at making a compliment sound like an insult!

'Drink it up,' he commanded savagely, as she stared broodingly down into the golden depth of her glass. 'Maybe it's not the finest liqueur, but it's time you learnt to rough it a bit.'

'I thought you had in mind to build up my strength?' she replied sweetly.

'Strength?' his dark brows lifted.

'Yes,' she smiled tauntingly again, 'sufficient to enable me to work hard enough, to ensure a quick payment of your rent.'

Instead of dismissing this lightly, as she had rather hoped he would, he jeered curtly, 'Fat chance I would have of getting anything if I relied on you, Miss Grant. You can't cook, you won't work, and now you prevent your mother from benefiting from the sub-letting of a field.'

Her glance was so laced with dislike it covered the odd pain. She took a fortifying gulp of beer, disregarding the foam which clung to her enticing upper lip. 'It

seems so ridiculous for a man like you to be hounding
your poor tenants.'

'Hounding?'

Taking no notice of the smoulder at the back of his
eyes, she ran the back of her hand across her damp
mouth. 'You could surely find some better sport?'

Ryan leant nearer, over the table, his eyes fixed on
her face as if daring her to look away. 'If this place
wasn't so public, Melissa, you wouldn't be able to sit
down for a week! You can thank your lucky stars I
don't take the rantings of an idle young woman seriously. I didn't bring you here to talk about your debts,
although, while we're on the subject, you might pause
and consider how it would be if word got around that
I was willing to be indulgent with tenants who didn't
pay up.'

Melissa had the grace to flush, knowing he was right
but not grateful to be put in her place. Rather her
hatred of him increased. 'You'll get your money!' she
said fiercely. 'Even if I have to borrow from one of my
friends.'

'What security could you offer?' he taunted.

'I have one friend,' she cried recklessly, 'who wants
to marry me.'

'So now,' Ryan Trevelyan said tightly, 'we're getting
to the truth. You'd be willing to sell yourself?'

'As you've just said,' she strove to be flippant, 'what
else have I to offer?'

He paused, his expression hard, his eyes on the perfect oval beauty of her face. 'It's interesting to learn
that you're for sale.' He reached suddenly and took her
slim hand in his, turning it over, examining the fragile,
pink-tipped fingers closely. 'You could be right. This
hand was never designed for market gardening.'

'Does everything have to be designed for hard work?'
she asked, scarcely knowing what she was saying, too
conscious of the impact of his gently massaging thumb.

'Certainly not,' his hand curled her wrist now, and
she felt his breath on her cheek, 'but in your case you

might be wiser to stick to it. You might find it easier to live with than a husband you don't really want.'

They were attracting considerable attention and he pulled her to her feet. 'For a girl who doesn't care for beer you got rid of that remarkably quickly. We'll get back before you take too much.'

Really, she thought, her heart reacting strangely as he almost dragged her out again, he didn't believe in giving her time to draw breath. He appeared to imagine he had her exactly where he wanted her and could treat her as he liked! His hand, which had somehow slipped to her narrow waist, hurt.

It wasn't the best moment to meet Angela Brett. She was in the company of a tall young man, some years younger than Ryan Trevelyan.

Angela's eyes flashed angrily when she saw who Ryan was with, but her smile was a masterpiece of surprised pleasure. 'Not going already, darling?' She gazed up at him, making no effort to conceal a considerable adoration. 'Why not join Peter and me for a drink? You, too, Miss Grant,' she added, more gracefully than she was obviously feeling.

Ryan muttered a short refusal before whisking Melissa away. 'Another time, Angela.' He nodded briefly to her companion, his lips tightening.

Could he be jealous? Melissa wondered, as they sped back to the smallholding. He looked grim, as if the sight of Angela with another man hadn't altogether pleased him. She asked, because she couldn't help it, 'Are you going to marry Angela Brett?'

His mouth relaxed in an exasperated sigh, his sideways glance taking in her frowning face. 'What makes you think you have the right to ask?'

'I haven't,' Melissa regretted her own impulsiveness. 'I was just curious, that's all. You don't have to answer. You looked so cosy having tea together at Poldary that I guessed.'

'You should never guess about things like that, Melissa. You're too full of curiosity and you could be jumping to all the wrong conclusions.'

Which didn't answer her query completely. Through the uneven beat of her pulse she retorted, 'It was your own curiosity you were talking about earlier.'

'So I was.' Without warning he pulled off the deserted road and, after switching off the engine, turned and grabbed her, pulling her shaking body right into his arms. 'This might explain what I was curious about.' His head lowered just as her stunned mind righted itself and she hit out at him, catching him across the face with a small clenched fist.

'You little bitch!' His anger flared harshly as he lifted his own hand and slapped her back. 'Women are always yelling about equal rights,' he rasped, 'so don't start complaining.'

'Then let me go!' Her cheek smarted and panic caused her voice to rise wildly. In spite of his warning, backed by the glitter in his eyes, she tried to lash out at him again, and she was aware that the glitter deepened as he controlled her by dragging her to him.

'I will let you go all in good time,' he said, 'when I've satisfied myself regarding one or two things.'

His hand moulded her fragile chin, turning her trembling mouth up to his, with a steely determination she couldn't dispute. Fright froze her so she was unable to struggle against the hard strength of him, the way his arms pressed her slim body against his own. Feverishly she told herself to keep calm, that it would soon be over, but she was totally unprepared for the passion which leapt between them like a flame as their lips met. It was like the first time, but much worse. As if he, too, felt that flash of magnetic current, his breath rasped, as he forced her mouth open with a punishing mastery. Multiple sensations seemed to shoot through her as excitement exploded in her head, invading every part of her. As his hands slid slowly and seductively over her, there came a brilliance of light against her tightly closed lids, a sheer wildness of sensation which rendered her helpless, although after the first few minutes she tried to pull away from him. She couldn't endure it, even while her senses urged her to surrender. Somehow she knew she had to fight this sweeping fever of the senses that threatened to take over completely.

Panic-stricken, she pushed against him with her hands, shrinking from the contact of his warm, rough skin as her frantic endeavours wrenched buttons from his shirt and her clawing fingers slid through the opening. Stunned, she felt the wanton impulse in them to linger and explore, to press her mouth to the thunderous beat of his heart and cling to the hard breadth of him. Fortunately, in time, her mind rejected this.

'Let me go!' As his forceful mouth eased, so he might look at her, she tore herself from his arms, her eyes sparkling angrily in her flushed face. 'If you think what we owe entitles you to extract payment whichever way you like, then you can think again! I've told you, I dislike being kissed.'

Savagely he grasped her arm. 'You can pretend to hate what you like, but I don't happen to believe you. I know all about the ones who play hard to get. You cry and protest a bit too much, Miss Grant. I don't think you could stop me taking anything, if I wanted to.'

Insensed, Melissa spat at him, 'You could be over-estimating your own attraction, Mr Trevelyan, as well as your ability to analyse the response of a girl you choose to kiss against her will.'

'I don't think so,' with a taunting smile his eyes rested keenly on her flushed face. 'You're fairly transparent, to me anyway. You're either stiff with pride or have had a fright of some kind, maybe way back in your half-forgotten childhood? It's going to be interesting finding out.'

'It's no business of yours, whichever way I'm made,' she spluttered nervously, determined he should never know of her problem—if this was what it really was? A reluctance to get too close to a man was perhaps not usual, but she couldn't agree it wasn't normal.

'At least I've cleared up one thing,' he muttered

tightly, and mysteriously. Then, as if losing interest, he turned from her and switched on the engine, apparently indifferent to her suddenly tormented face. When he dropped her off, he merely said curtly, 'Don't forget my party on Wednesday night. I'll expect to see you there.'

Not looking forward to, or will be delighted to see you, just—I expect! He commanded, dominated and expected to be obeyed. Even Angela Brett, who was obviously in love with him, was to be treated carelessly when he felt like it. Shuddering, Melissa stared after his departing car. She had thought he intended taking her out to discuss the problem of the top field, but this had scarcely been mentioned. She supposed his kisses, which he knew she hated, had been a kind of punishment for what he considered her idle selfishness in wanting to keep hold of something she had no use for. He didn't know his rough treatment of her was only making her more determined he shouldn't get it.

Her heart still full of fear and resentment, Melissa dressed for his party two nights later. She didn't want to go, but Mary had been so upset by her stubborn refusals, she had given in. To her surprise Mary and Lewis also decided they would go. Melissa had a shrewd suspicion this was to ensure she didn't run off somewhere else but, even so, she was glad of their company, especially when Lewis agreed not to drink too much. This was Mary's stipulation, not hers. Somehow Melissa hadn't found the courage to reproach him about his tendency to over-indulge. She had noticed he didn't go out nearly so much these days and seemed sober enough most of the time.

They were going by car, Mary's car, which had been returned from the garage as good as new. When Ryan rang to ask how they were travelling, she'd had the satisfaction of refraining from thanking him for it. After all, he expected to be paid for it, eventually. It was only after he rang off that she'd felt indescribably mean and wondered why he could so easily manage to make her act this way.

Mary, looking very smart in a dress she had renovated, insisted they have a small sherry in the lounge before leaving. Lewis, surprisingly distinguished in black jacket and tie, poured it out. Hit suddenly by suspicion that this pre-party drink had been planned with something definite in mind, Melissa waited wearily.

She didn't have to wait long. 'Melissa,' Mary began, pleading frankly, 'you won't do anything to antagonise Mr Trevelyan—Ryan, this evening, will you? It really is important, dear.'

Frowning, Melissa tried to make light of it. Must Mary worry about the damned rent all the time! 'I might not get an opportunity,' she said carelessly. 'He probably won't even notice I'm there.'

'Oh, he'll do that all right,' Mary assured her seriously. 'We've seen the way he looks at you, haven't we, Lewis?'

'Please,' Melissa's voice held stony impatience, though her heart beat incredibly fast, 'you'd be silly to imagine he was really interested, if that's what you're implying. He's the kind of man who might look at any new girl and, as I've already hinted, I think he's more than friendly with Angela Brett.'

'Sir Harry's daughter,' Mary neither confirmed nor denied it, but stood biting her lip unhappily. 'Her father bought Colonel Llewellyn's old place a few months after Ryan came.'

So that was why she couldn't remember Angela. Melissa spoke quickly, in order to cover a moment's unease. 'She sounds as if she would make Ryan a very suitable wife. And, while we're talking about him, you'd better let him know tonight, if you get the chance, that he can have the top field. You must tell him it has nothing to do with me. I don't know why I said anything in the first place, but we certainly have no right to hang on to it.'

'No!' Mary and Lewis exclaimed simultaneously,

while deliberately not looking at each other. Lewis shut up right away, as if it had been decided Mary should do the talking. Mary continued, smiling sweetly at Melissa, 'I don't think we'll say anything about the field unless it becomes strictly necessary. I know we aren't using it at present, but a few acres of good pasture are always useful to have by one.'

'But, if he wants it, we must let him have it!' Melissa stared at them in astonishment.

'Well, we'll see,' Mary smiled. 'We'll wait and see how you get on.'

'You mean——' Melissa went white, her eyes widening, 'you mean you'd be willing for me to have an affair with him just for the sake of a few pounds of rent?'

'It's more than just a few pounds, Melissa, as I've told you before. But never mind. You know I wouldn't want you to go as far as that, and you're an extremely foolish girl if you think so.' With a delicate shrug of her shoulders, she switched off the light, rushing her husband and daughter from the room. 'I suggest we forget the whole thing. We'll get to Poldary and enjoy ourselves.'

There was a bleak look in Melissa's eyes as she watched Mary talking to some of the other guests in the huge drawing room at Poldary. She knew now why Mary had grown more tolerant of late. She saw her daughter as someone she might use to further her own ends, just as Helen had done. Only where Helen's objective had been to procure a title for the family, Mary was grasping at any means possible to get herself out of her financial difficulties. The best thing she could do, Melissa decided, was to take herself off somewhere and leave Mary and Lewis to find their own way out of their present troubles.

Yet, even as the thought struck her, it seemed to smack too much of cowardice to be totally acceptable. Hadn't she run too often, first deserting Mary, then Helen? Perhaps her actions could be justified, but she didn't feel like doing the same thing again, not if she could help it. For better or worse she must stay and see her mother through her present troubles. After that she might feel free to do as she liked, away from the disapproving surveillance of a man like Ryan Trevelyan.

Broodingly, through the thick screen of her lashes, she watched him enter the room with Angela clinging to him like a limpet. She shivered to remember how she had felt in his arms, how her mouth still seemed to burn from the insidious pressure of his kisses. She would be revenged on him, she vowed, supposing it took her a hundred years! Deliberately, as her eyes met his across the sea of wandering guests, she turned her back on him and began smiling gaily at a group of young men who were clustering to meet her.

CHAPTER FOUR

MELISSA was glad she had ignored her conscience sufficiently to allow her taking two evening outfits when she left Helen's. One she wore this evening. It consisted of a fine silk slip on top of which she wore a matching lace tiered dress that dipped provocatively at the back. The high-heeled gold sandals which matched had, alone, cost almost forty pounds, but worn with sheer silk stockings, on Melissa's long, slim legs they looked worth every penny.

How quickly, with the donning of such expensive clothes, she found herself slipping back into her old, coolly sophisticated self. She chatted easily and lightly to the various young men who begged Mary for an introduction to her beautiful daughter. She pretended to be more interested than she actually was, as if some subconscious part of her wanted to punish Mary for the anxious glances she cast at Ryan each time Melissa's gay laughter rang out. If Mary's hopes in that direction hadn't seemed so obvious Melissa doubted if she would have laughed at all. Secretly she hoped Ryan would ignore her for the whole of the evening, little dreaming that, as far as that went, she was in for a shock.

The room was large and adequate space had been cleared for dancing. Mary had whispered that all Ryan's tenants appeared to be here, as well as a host of other people. Mrs Barr and a team of helpers had obviously been busy as the whole place was warm and welcoming and seemed quite different from how Melissa remembered it on her previous, more unfortunate visits.

As one of her new band of admirers spoke to her,

Melissa turned her head, inadvertently catching a glimpse of Ryan walking over to the small orchestra in the opposite corner. If he hadn't seemed to stand out, somehow, from every other man, she might not have noticed. He said something to the band leader, then strolled casually to the group which surrounded Melissa, But it wasn't until he stood beside her that the band struck up and, without even asking, he drew her smoothly into his arms.

'The first one for me, I think,' he moved her easily out among the other couples taking the floor. 'I hope your new friends aren't as disappointed as they look.'

'I suppose you always get your duty dances over first.' Melissa forced herself to go rigid as the expertise of his manoeuvre, if that was what it was, threatened to take her breath away. He hadn't even left her time to think of an excuse!

He moved with the smoothness of a panther and looked formidably attractive in his well tailored dinner jacket. 'I don't consider you that way, Miss Grant. Maybe I just wanted to have you in my arms, some place where you wouldn't find it easy to raise your usual objections.'

She was more frightened by the strange feeling that was taking over her body than his teasing words, yet she managed to speak coldly. 'I didn't really want to dance, with you or anyone. You must realise I have to help Mum keep an eye on Lewis?'

'Stop worrying, that's all taken care of.' He turned her dexterously at the end of the room. 'I've told you before, drinking isn't his real problem, and he'll get nothing more than a few drinks here tonight.'

'I hope you're right,' she frowned.

'Forget about Lewis,' he smiled suavely into her clouded face, his eyes scrutinising her perfect make-up. 'I barely recognised you when you arrived. Quite a transformation, and one I rather like, even if it looks costly.'

'Cousin Helen provided my clothes,' Melissa said

tersely. 'I brought two dresses with me. I shouldn't have done——'

'But you couldn't resist it,' he drawled, as her voice trailed off unhappily. 'One of these days you might be able to afford such clothes yourself.'

'So might pigs fly!' she muttered inelegantly.

He laughed tauntingly. 'If you worked a bit harder.'

'Mr Trevelyan!' she exclaimed fiercely, 'I——'

'I didn't mention what at,' he cut in mockingly. 'You always jump to the wrong conclusions.'

'I'd like to go back to my mother now,' she said quickly, hating him afresh for every reason she could think of—and more.

'I want you to come and meet some old friends from Australia.' He kept hold of her arm as the music seemed obligingly to stop. 'They arrived last night, unexpectedly. There are also a few others whom I'm sure you've not met, some who live in the district.'

Before she could prevent it he drew her over and began introducing her to Angela's parents. Angela's parents, she suspected, were snobs, but the Australians were nice. They were doing a world tour, a brother and two sisters. The two girls, around Angela's age, in their late twenties, seemed to adore Ryan, while their brother Ben stared at Melissa as if she were some form of enchantment conjured up from the dark reaches of Bodmin Moor.

Melissa, letting the devil in her take over, was charming to him—and she had been taught how to be very charming indeed. She danced happily with him, glad to get away from Ryan's dark glances, completely forgetting she had expressed a definite wish to return to Mary.

'Thank you, Ben,' she smiled when, to her surprise, Ryan claimed her for the next one. Her smile faded as she thought wistfully how easily she called this newcomer Ben while she still addressed Ryan as Mr Trevelyan. Of course Ryan had never suggested otherwise.

Deliberately, because there always seemed a challenge she must take up with him about something, she exclaimed with false brightness, 'You don't have to monopolise me completely, Ryan.' She couldn't prevent the faint bravado required to utter his name from colouring her cheeks.

'Don't be selfish,' he muttered, drawing her closer. 'If your host doesn't deserve to dance with his prettiest guest then I don't know who does.'

'You enjoy teasing me.'

'I can't altogether deny it,' he replied soberly, his cheek touching hers as he bent to her ear. 'Maybe it was the way you said my name. It could mean you feel you like me better.'

'I doubt it,' she retorted, perhaps too emphatically.

The lights lowered and, as if to punish her, his arms tightened around her, his hand as he did so slipping halfway into the provocative slit at the back of her dress. The touch of his fingers on her bare shoulder-blade caused her to stiffen as, once again, the blood in her veins seemed to melt. Her feelings taunted her. He seemed only to have to lay a finger on her and she was beset by urgent desires, as undeniable as they were indefinable. As, on previous occasions, she wanted to fight, yet wholly instinctively, before she could prevent it, she found herself twisting naturally to the sensuous throb of the music. Feeling her response Ryan's hand deliberately inserted itself a little further. As his mouth lowered to touch her cheek she felt his hand come round to her side, its pressure increasing as he moved it upwards a little, and she flinched, trembling beneath the wild onslaught of pleasure which flooded her. Her dreamy eyes opened wide, darkening with shame as she recovered her senses and jerked away from him.

'Please!' she gasped, her eyes accusing. 'Let me go!'

His hand, grasping her waist like an iron band, brought her cruelly back to him. 'You damned well asked for it,' he said curtly, drawing her unobtrusively into the shadows of a curtained alcove as the dance finished. 'And I'm not a man to refuse the kind of invitation you were throwing out. Whether you realised it or not you were practically begging to be made love to.'

'I was not, and you know it!' Frantically bewildered, Melissa tried to bluster her way out. She was more than relieved to find Angela by her side. Desperately she knew she had to get away for a minute alone, if only to sort out her feelings. Something was happening inside her and she wasn't sure she liked it, but surely she had never given the impression Ryan seemed to have?

'Hello, Angela,' she smiled uneasily, aware that Ryan's eyes hadn't left her—a fact which Angela, with her supreme confidence, didn't appear to notice.

'I've been looking for you, darling,' Angela pouted gracefully at Ryan. She didn't ignore Melissa but glanced at her insultingly. 'I'm sure you've done your duty for one night.'

'You could be right, my dear.' He gave Angela his whole attention, while Melissa went hot as she recalled how he had, only a short time ago, denied dancing with her for that reason. Men were nothing if not two-faced!

She met his bored gaze coldly before murmuring a quick excuse and disappeared into the crowd. She didn't need to look to see him gather Angela to him for the next dance, almost as closely as he had held her, nor to strain her small ears to hear his amused laughter as Angela said, 'You'll be giving her ideas above herself if you aren't careful, darling.'

Thinking this would be the end of it, seeing how much attention he showered on Angela and her parents, Melissa was too surprised to protest when Ryan swept her away for the supper dance. Scenes were not much in her line, but she had never felt more like making one! Did he have to go to such lengths to make Angela jealous? Taking a deep breath, she made herself endure in silence, unable again, after the first few moments, to think clearly against the temptation of his broad chest. He hummed light snatches of the popular song, 'It's now or never,' his cheek resting briefly on top of her burnished head, and as he whirled her with sardonic expertise, her body caught the tempo and she gave herself up to the heart-throbbing delight of it.

Then he announced that he was having supper with Mary, Lewis and herself, telling her protesting crowd of admirers they could have her back later. They sat at one of the many trestle-tables set out in the dining and morning rooms, and Melissa was conscious of Angela's furious face while she ate the delectable food.

'She looks as though she'd like to slap me,' she whispered to Mary—but was utterly astonished, later, when Angela did.

They were upstairs, in one of the bedrooms which was serving as a powder room, inadvertently alone together, when Angela exclaimed. 'I hope you don't imagine Ryan is attracted to you. He would never look seriously at a smallholder's daughter.'

'He's done more than that.' Melissa was ashamed to discover she could be as spiteful as anyone when she was attacked. Not that she felt too amused about the smallholder bit. Maybe it was true, but it stung her pride more than she liked to admit.

The surprise came when Angela struck. It was a forceful blow because Melissa wasn't expecting it and had no time to avoid it. She blinked the tears from her eyes as she nursed her stinging cheek—but Angela wasn't yet finished.

'You come here, like a cheap little siren, dressed as if you had nothing on at all!'

Ryan's words came hurtling back: I'm not a man to refuse that kind of invitation, and a flush of mortification deepened the red imprints of Angela's fingers. Had Angela overheard? Was her dress really that bad? Glancing down at it, Melissa saw how it clung lovingly to her slight form, emphasising the full curve of her breasts. Somehow her own body had never much interested her before. Now, although she was sure her dress was quite respectable, she felt herself going hot with embarrassment under Angela's despising stare.

Her chin lifted, pride coming belatedly to her aid. 'If you want a man you often have to fight for him, Angela, and if he wants a girl badly enough I don't think he would worry too much about where she came from.'

'Stop calling me Angela!' Angela's face went an ugly red and for a moment Melissa felt sorry for her, but only for a moment. 'When I'm Mrs Trevelyan,' Angela continued, 'I might allow you to call me Angela then.'

Melissa stared after her as the door slammed. Did Angela imagine she was offering an irresistible bribe? A sort of keep off the grass and you'll be rewarded gesture! Melissa felt stung and shaken both together and didn't know why, but she felt grateful when Mary asked if she was ready to go. When Ryan's narrowed eyes grimly scrutinised the still visible marks on her cheek she didn't attempt to enlighten him.

Next morning Melissa got the car out and drove back to Poldary. The morning was fine but cold and, as she left the car, she could hear the measured beat of the waves on the wild Atlantic shore. She loved this northern part of Cornwall, with its wild moor and great curves of cliff. The stark sea walls with jagged rocks lying at their foot in tumbled heaps made her shiver and think of smuggling days and remember the frightening stories her father used to tell of the escapades of some of his ancestors. But there was nothing of that now and the sheltered coves with their deep, hidden caves basked in relative peace and quiet.

Only a glimpse of the old pirates remained in the touch of aloofness about the people, a sombre darkness and strength of character which lingered from the grim, hard past. It was strange how she seemed to catch a glimpse of it in Ryan Trevelyan, when his face darkened with anger and passion. Yet Ryan hadn't been born here, nor, to her knowledge, had he ever lived here until his elderly cousin died.

Standing by the car in silent contemplation for a moment, Melissa sighed. She was going riding with Ben, the Australian. He had refused to take no for an answer the night before, and recalling what Ryan had said about his horses not getting enough exercise, Melissa had suddenly agreed, not because she really wanted to go out with Ben, but she fancied it would annoy Ryan. Annoying Ryan seemed to have become the kind of game she couldn't resist. Ben was Ryan's guest. If he thought it all right to invite someone to ride at Poldary, she wasn't going to argue.

She found her way to the stables quite easily, having been there often as a child. Ben was waiting for her with a young mare already saddled, and if he appeared a little startled by her shabby jeans and sweater, after her elegance at the party, he was too polite to make any comment. It seemed enough for him that she had turned up.

The fine weather held and they had an enjoyable gallop, walking the horses in companionable silence after their first freshness wore off. She felt so safe with Ben she wasn't surprised to learn how his father owned a big sheep station in Queensland.

'Ryan has an interest in the station next door,' he enlightened her. 'This is how we know him.'

'But,' she was round-eyed, 'he can't ever be there?'

Ben grinned. 'You'd be surprised! Of course he has other interests in New Zealand where he still spends quite a lot of time.'

Trying to ignore the dismay that washed over her to think Ryan must probably be gone for months, she concentrated instead on her disgust. Fancy plaguing Mary for her paltry rent when he must be very well off indeed! She told herself he was despicable and that she was pleased he might soon be away.

That didn't stop her heart from thumping to discover him waiting for them when Ben and she returned. His face was thunder-cloudish and he didn't try to hide the fact that he was displeased.

He glanced curtly at Melissa and spoke quietly to Ben. 'You'd better go in to breakfast. The girls are waiting to see you.' He didn't say anything about Melissa having breakfast and Ben hesitated, his eyes fixed on the pink, glowing sheen of her windblown cheeks, but when he seemed likely to argue, Ryan said firmly, 'Now!'

'Oh, sure.' Reluctantly Ben passed his reins to Ryan, who led the horse to his loose box, disposing swiftly of the saddle and giving the animal a quick rub down. His eyebrows rose as he saw Melissa had managed very well on her own.

'You're quite efficient in some ways, Miss Grant.'

Her eyes flew over him. In his open-necked shirt, his powerful forearms bared, he looked the arch-enemy and just as scaring. Melissa tried to tell herself she wasn't afraid. 'I'm more efficient than you're polite,' she mumbled, 'so there's no need to be sarcastic. I could have done with a cup of tea.'

'Could you, indeed?' He stopped what he was doing and came over to her, but made no promise to supply one. 'I told you, didn't I, I would take you riding, if you wanted to go?'

Because she had no ready excuse she made a joke of it, or attempted to. 'Foreign visitors should be entertained.'

'Stop trying to be funny,' his eyes darkened with anger on her defiant tones. 'I want you to leave Ben alone. He's not for you.'

'No one's for me, it seems.' Her laughter came a little hysterically, as Ryan frowned.

It was as if he was remembering something. 'Hadn't you a mark on your cheek last night, as you left?'

He was never going to know! She wouldn't give him the chance of defending Angela for her own bitchiness. Melissa didn't blink an eyelid. 'I bumped into one of your cupboard doors upstairs. I promise you I didn't damage the cupboard.'

'I see,' his mouth curled at one corner. 'If I said I didn't believe you, you might only hatch up another tale, so we'll leave it.'

Suddenly Melissa saw red. 'If I told you Miss Brett took a swipe at me would you believe that?'

'I might,' he returned calmly, 'but I would want to know what you'd done to provoke her. Angela is the mildest of girls.'

She stared at him disdainfully, trying to transmit her hate silently, deciding she would rather die than attempt any kind of explanation with him feeling as he did.

Ryan sighed, obviously keeping a tight rein on his growing impatience, as he changed the subject abruptly. 'Who taught you to ride? You've a good seat.'

She was as relieved to talk of something else as he seemed to be. 'Helen kept some horses.'

'And you enjoy riding. Perhaps you're hoping to wangle an invitation out of Ben to go to Australia. He seems quite interested.'

'Well, I'm not. I don't care for men.' She turned from him, presenting a contemptuous shoulder. Indifferently she said, 'I suppose you've a right to feel annoyed because I rode one of your horses, but Ben assured me it would be all right.'

'He could only have been guessing. Next time ask me.'

'I probably won't bother.'

She had meant she wouldn't bother riding again, but he had to interpret it the wrong way. 'You little bitch!' His hands caught her, holding her like a vice. 'I don't have to put up with everything you choose to ladle out. You don't like men, you definitely flinch when one kisses you, so perhaps it's the most effective form of punishment.'

The light was dim in the stable, she could barely see him properly, but instinctively she knew his mouth was descending. 'No!' she cried. 'Please!' In panic she twisted her head, so his lips merely grazed her cheek, but he didn't appear to mind.

It was as if he expected such a reaction and was ready to deal with the least hint of opposition. He took no notice of her anguished whisper, just shrugged as he gathered her closer as if he had all the time in the world.

'Take your hands off me!' she fumed, but his hard eyes mocked her angry terror as he raked determined fingers through her hair. Quickly, as she read his intention, she lifted her foot, kicking him hard on his leg.

'Hell!' he swore roundly, his face darkening with anger to match her own, and the momentary relaxing of his hold gave her the chance to beat at him with clenched hands, as all her old fright surfaced in rising hysteria.

'Heaven help you!' he ground out, 'if it's a battle you want——'

He lifted her, as easily as he might a feather, and she saw the direction he was taking towards a dark annexe filled with hay. The hay was loose and soft, but a sharp cry escaped her as she felt herself thrown on to it and the weight of him coming down on top of her took her breath away. She seemed to lie in a suffocating delirium as, with anger driving him, he grasped her sweater, tearing it over her head. Then his fingers began slowly to unbutton the thin shirt she wore underneath, and she seemed to have no strength left to stop him.

'If you don't like kisses perhaps there are other things?'

His voice came to her from a distance, but his breath was rough on her face and she suddenly found herself unable to reply. As he thrust the opened shirt from her bare shoulders the warmth within her mocked the morning cold. Last night she had wanted to know what it felt like to have his hands exploring her body. Now she stiffened, then gave a groan as a violence of sensuous feeling swept over her. As he muttered something and held her closer she moaned again, in a mixture of pleasure and fear. This time when he sought her mouth she made no attempt to avoid him, but clung to him tightly as though she were drowning.

Out in the yard there came the sound of tractors moving, of loud shouts which penetrated even the thick stable walls, warning them that they didn't have the world completely to themselves. Even so, Ryan didn't hurry to release her lips, to take his hands off her. When he did he passed her sweater, his face impassive, as if there was nothing extraordinary about being here with her in the hay.

'My men seem to have a worse sense of timing than I have,' he said mockingly. Yet his eyes were keen on her hotly flushed face as he got up calmly, dragging her with him.

During the next few days Melissa heard rumours—and some gossip first hand. Mrs Barr came to the shop and while Melissa weighed vegetables in the back, she overheard her telling Mary that Angela Brett was never away from Poldary and that Mr Trevelyan must be attracted to her. She also heard from Ben, who had prolonged his visit to Poldary and was frequently at the shop, that his elder sister still fancied him.

'You're getting very popular,' she said sarcastically, when Ryan next came in for his newspaper. 'Don't you mind people talking about you? I believe they're laying wagers in the village as to who'll get you, Angela or one of the Australian young ladies.'

Regarding his stern face, Melissa wasn't sure how she had the nerve to speak to him as she did, unless the three occasions—she counted them regularly—when he had kissed her, were responsible for her incredibly reckless mood. If she hadn't felt so mysteriously discouraged and miserable over Mrs Barr's talk ...

For an odd moment, as he frowned, she felt something bothered him. If he hadn't been so formidably self-contained she might have thought she was right. But the impression was fleeting and completely gone when he said, 'You have a great imagination. I know what I want and it's never wise to speculate. I expect it's your own curiosity you're trying to satisfy, rather than anyone else's.'

She stared at him haughtily, fighting not to recall his arms and his mouth, to remember their impact. 'You must excuse me, I'm busy.'

'It's years since I stopped taking hints,' he rejoined coolly his glance wandering deliberately over her until it seemed every bit of her had been thoroughly examined. He paused on her hands, the two broken nails, their roughened appearance. 'Can't you find a pair of old gloves?' he asked curtly, flicking his eyes to her dishevelled cloud of dark red hair. 'You don't have to make a martyr of yourself.'

Melissa retorted sweetly, 'I thought nothing less would satisfy you, Mr Trevelyan? I assure you I have no intention of becoming such a thing. I'm only here this morning because Mum isn't well again. Lately I've been helping in the greenhouses because I've always been interested in growing things, and they seem to have been suffering from neglect. There's a lot to be done, and Lewis isn't over-conscientious.'

Ryan didn't seem impressed. 'Not over-bothered by loyalty, are you? Your stepfather does know his job.'

'When he applies himself, yes,' she couldn't deny the truth of it. She frowned, looking at him more anxiously than she realised. 'You said, at your party, that drink wasn't Lewis's real problem, and he certainly doesn't seem to drink as much as he used to. Would you mind telling me what it is?'

'Ask your mother,' he replied sardonically.

'I gave up asking her anything a long time ago.'

He came nearer, grasping her arm, staring down at her.

'You've a bee in your bonnet about your mother, haven't you? Isn't it time you forgave and forgot whatever it is?' His eyes narrowed on the flawless curve of her mutinous mouth. 'You accuse me of being secretive, yet you play the same game yourself.'

'It's my own business.'

'You always come up with the same answer. You could try being more original for a change.' He shook her suddenly then flung her from him. 'I don't know why I bother!' he exclaimed.

She hadn't the sense to leave it there. 'You bother because of your miserable rent,' she cried, trying to conceal the unexpected tears in her eyes as she rubbed her smarting arms. 'I suppose this is how you come to be so well off? Taking care of the pennies so the pounds will take care of themselves.'

'Meaning?'

She should have been warned by the hardness of his face, but Cousin Helen had always encouraged her to speak frankly, believing that by nurturing a little arrogance, Melissa would have more appeal for the kind of people she wanted her to know. Now Melissa tilted her head defiantly, her green eyes glowing with contempt. 'You have property in other parts of the world, or so I've been told. You must be fairly wealthy, yet here you are, hounding us for a few miserable pounds!'

'Shut up!'

Somehow, Melissa didn't know why, she did. She found herself trembling, with a shaken reaction to her outburst, but he didn't appear to notice. He looked as if he would liked to have slapped her across his knee. 'So, God help me, I've taken about all I'm going to take from you! You don't know the meaning of co-operation. I've a good mind to take the place from your mother, here and now. I'd be quite within my rights.'

'You couldn't!' There was a horrible feeling in the pit of her stomach that disaster was about to strike and she was responsible.

His dark face was implacable. 'I do happen to know what I'm talking about. Didn't you believe me when I mentioned it before? Apart from this, Miss Grant, what are people going to say when they learn how much rent you owe?'

'You wouldn't.'

'Have no doubt,' he bit out, his eyes cold, 'I might amuse myself with insolent little girls, but they never appeal to my better nature. Take the holding back? I would!'

Dully Melissa's eyes seemed riveted to the shop door as it slammed. She seemed to have put her foot in it again and inexplicable emotions raced through her. It was clear, from Ryan's face, he would never forgive her. Not that she felt much like forgiving herself for perhaps stupidly jeopardising the situation for Mary, but there was a new unhappiness in Melissa's heart she couldn't account for and the tears she had blinked back a few minutes ago threatened to overflow.

'Damn him!' she muttered weakly, hating the treacherous ache in her throat. It was foolish to allow his threats to disturb her. He would be here tomorrow.

But he wasn't and, as the days went by without him coming near, she began to realise he might mean everything he said. She told herself she didn't care and put down the despair, which seemed to gnaw at her continually, as depression about the future, but Ryan's darkly forbidding face came between her and most things she did. In an attempt to divert her thoughts away from him she had dinner twice with Ben, but whether Ryan knew of these outings she didn't know. Ben actually professed to being in love with her and didn't want to leave the district, but couldn't get out of the arrangements already made for the continuance of his world tour. He went off reluctantly to America after assuring Melissa he and his sisters would be spending another week at Poldary on their way home to Australia.

Mary soon wanted to know why Ryan had stopped calling. She seemed more put out about this than Melissa thought possible, and she felt terribly guilty when she was forced to confess that she had quarrelled with him about the farm.

'I'm sorry, Mum,' she tried to laugh but failed as she

saw Mary's dismayed face. 'He provoked me and I said more than I intended——'

Mary flung out her hands helplessly. 'But why? You know what a fix we're in, and he liked you well enough. At the party he gave he never seemed to take his eyes off you. I heard several people asking who you were, so others must have noticed besides myself.'

'You imagine things, Mum!'

'I'm a woman, Melissa.' Mary was not to be side-tracked. 'Perhaps that's what's wrong with you.' She gazed at her daughter bitterly. 'Maybe you've never learnt to be one. Isn't it time you grew up?'

I grew up a long time ago, Melissa felt like retorting bleakly, but she didn't really want to hurt Mary more. 'Why don't you retire, Mum?' she asked instead. 'I know I've suggested it before, but wouldn't it be something, to be able to tell Ryan Trevelyan what to do with his smallholding?'

'I don't think I could ever leave here.' Mary's face seemed to grow pinched and old at even the thought of it. 'At least,' she frowned anxiously, 'I suppose I could if we had enough money to retire and buy a house in the village.'

'We could rent one.' Melissa felt she was getting somewhere at last.

Mary sighed. 'You don't understand. Nothing is ever rented these days. Houses, around here at any rate, are almost always sold, and at prices far beyond my pocket.'

Melissa tried again. 'Couldn't Lewis find a job, something with accommodation?'

'No,' Mary shook her head wearily, 'he wouldn't like that. And what could he do?—he isn't trained for anything. I know he has a degree, but that was years ago and he never did anything specific with it. I doubt if anyone would give him employment, especially at his age.'

Melissa faltered, 'Do you really think Ryan is preparing to throw us out next month?'

'He'd be entitled to, and I couldn't blame him.'

Mary's grimace was raw. 'I'd feel compelled to go, too, if we can't find enough to pay. I just can't live on charity for ever.'

'Mum,' Melissa looked her mother straight in the face so that she couldn't avoid answering, 'I want the truth. Ryan always hinted that drinking wasn't Lewis's worst fault. Will you tell me what is?'

'Gambling.' Mary's voice was stark, but on the whole she looked relieved at not having to hide it any more.

'Gambling!' Melissa's eyes widened with surprise, rather than horror. She'd seen plenty of gambling when she'd been abroad. The fashionable casinos where sophisticated, well-dressed men and women groaned and laughed, depending on their luck, around the gaming tables. Where life seemed to revolve on the toss of the dice, the spin of the roulette, where fortunes were often made and lost overnight. Helen had enjoyed a flutter, although she had known when to stop, and never had she allowed Melissa to do more than look over her shoulder. From this vantage point, however, Melissa would have been blind not to have noted the havoc such games could cause, the pain which so often had seemed to far outweigh the pleasure.

But surely this couldn't be the kind of thing Lewis indulged in, not in these parts? 'What sort of gambling?' she asked quickly, covering her startled pause.

'Oh, anything and everything,' Mary was vague. 'There's quite a wide choice if one knows where to look,' she faltered, 'but I hope he's cured now. I'm afraid, though, it took all our savings and more to convince him it's a mug's game. He's had help, of course.'

Still partly stunned by Mary's disclosure, Melissa glanced at her wryly. 'We'll just have to hope the cure is permanent and that Ryan doesn't press too hard for his money.'

'I don't think anything could help much, not at this late hour,' Mary shrugged, 'not even the coming tourist season. Lewis helps but he doesn't seem to realise the seriousness of the situation.'

It occurred to Melissa that this might be a good chance to reproach her mother again for marrying such a man, but somehow she found she couldn't do it. What would be the use? The thought came, rather belatedly, that perhaps her mother had suffered enough, and such an argument could make little difference now and might only make Mary more unhappy.

Instead she concentrated her bitterness on Ryan Trevelyan, putting from her mind that there were days when she longed to see him. No wonder he had been so sure he wouldn't get the money they owed him! It seemed unforgivable that he hadn't told her about Lewis's gambling but left her to imagine it was something less serious. Well, Mr Trevelyan could do his worst, for all she cared, but if he imagined she was going to work her fingers to the bone, he would find himself very much mistaken!

CHAPTER FIVE

TWICE after this momentous talk with Mary Melissa saw Ryan with Angela Brett. And another time, when she was sitting alone in a hotel tea-room in one of the local towns, they came in together. They didn't see Melissa, not right away, so she was able to study Ryan intently and wonder why, even at this distance, he had the ability to make her heart beat faster.

She watched furtively as a smiling waitress brought them cream cakes and scones, chatting to them for a few moments as if they were regular customers. Melissa hadn't been able to afford anything to eat, for all she had felt hungry. It had been extravagant, she knew, to so much as order a pot of tea in a high-class establishment like this, but it was the kind of place she had been used to frequenting with Helen and, for once, she hadn't been able to resist it.

Silly things, silver teapots and fine bone china, she thought morosely, while the remembered strength of Ryan's arms sent unexpected shivers down her spine. It was even sillier to regret not being able to afford them when she had discovered, since coming back home, that earthenware cups and saucers served the same purpose just as well. Yet sometimes she felt if she didn't dream a little she might go slightly mad. It was then that Ryan turned his head and saw her. He looked straight at her, sitting so incongruously in her shabby clothes in such smart surroundings, and she saw his mouth tighten.

Involuntarily, Melissa's thoughts went back to the night of his party, to the tune that was played while she danced with him, how her heartbeats had quickened as he had hummed odd snatches of it against her cheek. The next morning, in the stables, how her fingers had trembled so much she could scarcely do up the buttons of her blouse after he had left her. Looking now into his enigmatical eyes, across the space which divided them, she recalled these things and fancied somehow that he did too.

Then Angela, glancing to see what was taking Ryan's attention, saw her and her clear, strong voice broke the spell. 'It's regrettable the kind of people they allow into places like this nowadays.'

Melissa, feeling the full impact of her cold stare, wrenched her eyes away from Ryan's. Stumbling to her feet, her tea forgotten, she pressed two notes into the astonished waitress's hand without pausing for the change. It seemed ironical that it would have more than bought the sandwiches she had longed for. As it was she had scarcely touched her tea.

Later, as she purchased the goods Mary had sent her for, she felt so frozen up inside she hardly knew what she was doing.

When Mary told her they wouldn't be able to pay the rent, the news came as no surprise. She only felt a dull apprehension. It was what her mother said next that startled her.

'It's a week past the deadline, Melissa, and I had a phone call from Ryan this morning. He wants to see us, all of us, after lunch. You notice we aren't asked for lunch?' The look she shot at Melissa was laced with bitterness. 'If you'd managed things better we might have been.'

Melissa merely shrugged. She had known the date set by Ryan had passed but had ignored it, believing he would too. Now she said quickly, 'I don't think he'll want to see me. I'm sure you must be mistaken, Mum.'

'He specially stipulated that you should be there,' Mary insisted. 'He sounded as if he'd easily come and drag you to Poldary if you don't do as he asks.'

Poldary, basking in early summer sunshine, was a pleasant sight, but for once Melissa was blind and deaf to the appeal of it. Ryan met them at the door and

ushered them into the morning room. 'I thought we
could all sit around the table,' he explained evenly.

Melissa was conscious of cold, but then she had felt
cold ever since Mary had told her Ryan wanted to see
them, which was only hours ago but seemed like years.
Yet she allowed none of this deep foreboding to show
but fixed on her face an expression of careless, even
amused indifference. While aware, from the narrow
way he studied her, that such a brash front could be
dangerous, she made no attempt to alter it. Lifting her
chin a little, she even managed a faint smile which she
hoped expressed boredom, rather than the horrible
sinking feeling inside her.

Ryan, she noticed, was casually dressed, but in his
open-necked shirt with sleeves rolled up he emanated
a strong masculinity. On a purely physical level she
was conscious of his virile maleness, of something in
his gaze which quickened her breath. Momentarily she
closed her eyes as a sensation of warmth swept suddenly
over her.

He poured Lewis a drink and passed Mary and
Melissa sherries. Mary was waiting with the resigned
air of one already doomed and Melissa, glancing at her,
found her temper rising. Why had Ryan found it necessary to subject her mother to all this? Surely a brief
letter through his solicitor would have been a quicker
and kinder way of ending it all. It would have been
better to have made it legal and impersonal, rather
than drawing it out to the bitter end.

Restlessly Melissa sighed as she twiddled with her
glass, unconsciously giving the impression that she
couldn't care less while, all the time, something inside
her seemed to be tearing her apart and she couldn't
think why.

Ryan spoke first, his voice curt, his face so dark she
could see he meant business. He looked straight at
Melissa so she knew his opening remark was aimed
solely at her. 'Now, if the charade is over, we might get
something sorted out. If you don't stop playing with

your glass, Melissa, I'll take it from you.'

Her brief, 'Sorry,' touched on insolence and his mouth tightened.

He appeared to restrain himself with effort and turned to Mary·and Lewis, his eyes a shade kinder. 'You realise, I suppose, why I asked you to come and see me.'

'I'm sorry, Ryan,' Mary flushed slightly, 'I don't think you had much choice. We can't raise the money to pay one year's rent, never mind three, and I'm afraid I can't see the situation improving. The little we've made this year has been barely enough to keep us in food and clothing. Since——' her voice faltered, and she too obviously avoided looking at Lewis, 'Since our capital went, you see, we haven't been able to get enough together to pay for even such basic things as seed and fertiliser which is essential to grow produce for sale in the summer months. As for re-stocking with the usual commodities to be found in any good market garden shop—well, it's just been impossible.'

'So,' Ryan said quietly, as she came to a halt, 'you feel you've come to the end of the road?'

Mary nodded bleakly. 'I'm not here to beg for sympathy. No matter how I've tried to convince myself otherwise, I think that just about sums it up. I'm sorry,' she repeated.

'Don't be too despondent,' Ryan smiled faintly, 'not yet. This is why I called you here today.' He stared again at Melissa, his eyes hardening. 'Your daughter may not appreciate it, but I would like to help.'

'I don't think we want your help, Mr Trevelyan,' Melissa cried angrily, too raw from her last encounter with him to be cautious. She remembered his hateful smile when she had seen him with Angela in the hotel. When she had almost tripped over her feet in her haste to be gone. She added bitterly, before Mary could prevent her, 'In fact, I'm damned sure we don't.'

'Be quiet—I'll deal with you in a minute.' The grimness of his tones reduced her to a quivering silence and, before she could recover her shattered courage, he was speaking again to Mary, diverting her horrified attention from her too wayward daughter. 'We'd better begin by taking a look at the whole situation,' he said. 'You owe me three years' rent, plus a small sum you borrowed and the repairs for your car.' Swiftly he totalled up a sum to which Mary nodded confirmation as he jotted down the figure.

Ignoring Melissa's small gasp of dismay at the unexpected size of the amount, he asked quietly, 'Would you like me to write if off, Mary?'

'No!' Mary was on her feet, her dismay obvious. Then suddenly, like a burst balloon, she subsided, her face a study of despair. 'Thank you, Ryan. I know you mean well, but the answer must be no. Yet I don't see how we're going to repay you, it would only be adding to what we already owe—to ask you to give us more time. Whatever work we find to do, after we leave the holding, will probably be poorly paid. I don't think it would be possible for me to go back to teaching after all this time and, even if I could, teachers don't receive very high salaries.'

Ryan stopped her there. 'Before you go any further, I have one or two suggestions to make which you might like to consider, before you decide to do anything final.'

Melissa, her anger half forgotten, stared at him curiously. What could he suggest that Mary hadn't already tried? He spoke with such cool authority it was easy to imagine he could solve their problems, any problem, if he set his mind to it, but in his case, such generosity could only spring from a perverted desire to amuse himself at their expense. Surely Mary could see this? As his next words droned over her head she gazed down numbly at her fingers.

'Miss Grant! Have you listened to one word I've said?'

His voice jerked her like a whiplash and she flushed painfully, holding herself stiffly, as if the defences she had erected against him must be held at all cost.

'I've been discussing the options left open to you,

while you've been day-dreaming. You could leave the holding and hope to pay off the debt eventually, but, as you may have heard, this doesn't appeal to your mother. The alternative I offer may not appeal to you, but it could be a possible solution. You could all stay on and work for me. I would pay you wages and re-stock the place. This way you might soon pay off what you owe, and your mother can, if she wishes, retain the right to take over as a tenant again once your debt is cleared. It will, of course, mean a great deal of extra work, all of which I will personally supervise.'

Far from feeling grateful, as he appeared to think she ought to be, Melissa widened her eyes with repugnance. Where was Mary's pride that she could even listen to such a diabolical scheme? Could even contem-plate the humiliation of having Ryan Trevelyan stand-ing over them? It didn't say much for her love of her husband if she was willing to subject him to Ryan's continual surveillance! 'Who is going to do all this extra work?' she hissed, hating the look of dawning hope on her mother's face.

'You are,' he replied grimly, overriding her gasp of refusal. 'You're going to do a lot more than you're do-ing now! You're going to be so tired, Miss Grant, you won't have the energy to spare to insult me.'

Melissa turned to Mary, but she was too absorbed to come to her rescue. Mary, she saw furiously, was gazing at Ryan blindly, the sheen of grateful tears in her eyes. 'We haven't gone into all the details but, on the face of it, it sounds wonderful, Ryan. But why should you go to such trouble?'

'That's just where you're wrong,' he said smoothly. 'It will be a pleasure, not trouble. I've been interested in horticulture for a long time and this will provide an ideal opportunity to go into it thoroughly. Theory isn't much good without practice, you know. I could find myself proved wrong, rather than right, but I believe, properly run, without too great a drain on its resources, your holding could be very profitable, Mary.'

'You can count me out!' Melissa jumped up hotly as a strange panic seized her. 'You're not going to make me work like a servant! At least, not for you!'

'I can and you will!' Ryan looked at her with such emphatic deliberation that her legs gave way and she sat down again weakly. Never before had a man spoken to her like this!

'You can't force me,' she tried to stare at him fearlessly. 'I had nothing to do with what happened.'

At her continued defiance his face went cold. It was the face of a stranger, not of a man who had once held her and kissed her, lightly teased her. Melissa realised then that what little regard he had had for her was gone and that his dislike was probably stronger than her own. If dislike was what she really felt for him?

Her heart beating dully, she heard him say clearly and coldly, above the small, placating murmurs Mary was making, 'If you don't go along with this, Miss Grant, I can easily sue your parents for debt. I realise they could probably only be made to pay a small weekly sum for the rest of their lives and, from my point of view, seeing how the law usually favours the criminal, it would scarcely be worth it, but you would be responsible for the publicity which would undoubtedly affect your mother adversely.'

Mary's face was pale but, to Melissa's astonishment, she also seemed relieved, as if she was somehow glad of Ryan's frankness. She even stared at Melissa with some of his coldness, as if she, too, would hold her responsible for what happened if she didn't do as Ryan commanded.

Feeling near to tears, Melissa met his narrowed eyes, eyes which surveyed her impassively. 'My God, you're hard!' she burst out.

'Not as hard as I intend to be.'

Wildly, before such supreme ruthlessness, she attacked from another direction. 'What are people going to think when they see you practically standing over us all the time?'

His answer was ready, as she might have known it would be. 'If anyone actually confronts you about it you could imply that your parents and I have formed some kind of partnership. You can be as vague as you like, but I shouldn't like to think my frequent visits to the market garden might be construed for a different reason.'

Melissa's eyes flickered down to the table, to hide what was in them. Quite clearly he didn't want anyone to imagine he was coming to the holding to see her. Or was it only Angela he was worried about? This seemed more likely.

She heard Mary saying it was quite usual, these days, for firms to do this kind of thing and she was sure everything would be all right. Then she repeated how grateful she was to be given another chance. This Ryan brushed politely aside. He told her that he would be along next morning to go into everything thoroughly but that there shouldn't be any insurmountable difficulties. There was only one real problem, so far as he could see, but as it was one he must deal with himself she wasn't to worry about it.

He rose, which seemed to suggest the meeting was over. Lewis, whose sole contribution to the drama of the afternoon had lain in the occasional nodding and shaking of his head, heaved himself to his feet, assuring Ryan he would do his best. He was just like a sheep, Melissa thought sullenly, feeling not unlike one herself. None of them had found it possible to effectively oppose Ryan's plans. Lewis had probably realised, more wisely than she had done, to go against Ryan openly was simply a waste of time. The only way to fight a man like Ryan Trevelyan was behind his back. If you knew where to begin. Perhaps it might be better to start with Mary, once they were home again.

They were almost at the door when Ryan's voice halted her abruptly. 'I'll take you home later, Melissa. There are one or two things I'd like to discuss with you.'

Swinging around, Melissa protested, 'I don't think we have anything left to say to each other!' Hoping it would end there, she was dismayed to find herself almost thrust back into the morning room. The sound of Lewis driving off seemed like the knell of doom to her anxious ears. Fright moved swiftly through her but, rather than give him the satisfaction of knowing it, she merely shrugged her slim shoulders.

'We aren't going to talk to each other.' In spite of this promise, his words had an ominous ring to them and she was hard put to disguise a shudder. 'I simply want your promise of co-operation. I don't want you going to work on Mary the minute my back is turned, changing her mind. I don't trust you.'

'Then how could you believe any promise of mine?' she challenged fiercely.

'I don't.' He glanced at her indifferently, as he poured himself another drink. 'You're nothing but a spoiled, unprincipled little baggage and I realise there's nothing for it but to put the fear of death into you.'

'By more or less blackmailing me into working for you? You made yourself fairly clear before, if I can really believe you meant it!'

'Every word,' he promised silkily, 'but I was aware of your doubts. That's why I have to make sure you don't go away with the wrong impression. You stay, and you work or the deal's off.'

As if his stipulation was red hot, her mind veered wildly from it. 'I may have been spoiled a little,' she cried, 'I suppose Helen did allow me a lot of my own way, but I won't have it that I'm unprincipled!'

'What if I have proof?' he taunted.

'Proof?'

'Yes.' He half drained his glass, looking at her squarely. 'Can you deny you told Angela, at the end of the party I gave, that you thought Ben rather fancied you and it might pay you to string him along? She confessed she had struck you because of this. Momentarily she was overcome by disgust and horror, and I can't say I blame her.'

Melissa wanted to shout, that's not true! I never so much as mentioned Ben to Angela. I only met him that night! Instead, she said bleakly, 'You believed her?'

'Why not?' he shrugged. 'She mentioned it the other day, at that hotel. If she'd been out to make trouble she could have told me sooner. It was when you seemed to panic and rushed out without drinking your tea that it suddenly occurred to her you might be feeling too embarrassed to stay and face her. However, your principles, or rather the lack of them, isn't really what I wanted to talk about today.'

'How very kind you are, Ryan,' she sneered, holding back her hurt and anger with difficulty. 'This past hour your charitable nature has been fully demonstrated, especially regarding Angela Brett! You might think you can hoodwink Mum and Lewis easily, but you don't deceive me. It's simply a lust for power which makes you act as you do. Nothing else comes into it!'

'If you don't shut up,' he spoke between his teeth, 'I'll wallop the daylights out of you! You'll be up to-morrow at six and into those greenhouses. Some stable girls I know rise at four.'

'But I'm not one of your stable girls, Mr Trevelyan! And I don't see how you can hold me responsible for Lewis's gambling debts. Yes, I know now this was what took all Mum's money! I might have guessed. I always knew he was weak and, if you remember, I didn't want her to marry him.'

'Yes,' Ryan's mouth curled as much as her own, 'you told me all about running away. What you overlooked to mention was that for years your mother fretted over your going, blaming herself and, indirectly, Lewis. You could say it was this atmosphere which subconsciously drove him to seeking such diversions.'

'Oh, no!' Melissa went cold, her eyes tormented. 'You can't be serious?'

'I couldn't seriously suggest a mere child to be wholly

responsible for her actions, but you get the drift?'

'Oh, yes, Mr Trevelyan!' Melissa's coldness changed to hot contempt. 'I get that all right. You choose to believe your beautiful girl-friends. Anything, anyone but me! I'm to be punished for things I never said, for crimes I've never committed. At least,' her eyes clouded unhappily, 'at least ...'

'Yes?' he prompted tersely.

'Oh, nothing.' What was the use of confessing that she had realised too late she could have been wrong about many things? It would be too much like admitting failure. Steadying her breath, she went on, 'I think we've strayed too far from the subject you kept me here to talk about. You may not think me a good market-gardener, but I could never imagine you being one. What about the times you have to go abroad? You won't be able to see what I get up to then, will you?'

'Long before I go away again,' he assured her, 'you'll be nicely programmed to do exactly as I want.' With a faint gleam in his eyes he poured a second drink, putting it into her hands, 'A reward for that touch of humility.'

'How very kind of you!' With a tantalising flick of curling lashes, which for an odd moment seemed to stop him in his tracks, she raised her glass, but instead of drinking from it, some devil of perversity caught her and she hurled it with all her strength into the huge stone fireplace. As it shattered into a thousand shining fragments she stared at it with a horrified blankness.

She started to say something, but before she could move her paralysed lips he had grabbed her. Hauling her to him, he began shaking her without mercy, his hands biting cruelly into her shoulders, blind and deaf to her frantic cries of protest. Helplessly she bit her lip hard to prevent herself screaming and when he released her a trickle of blood ran from her bruised mouth in a thin stream. Through the painful pounding of her heart she heard him speaking, a thickness in his voice she put down to anger.

'I'm sorry if I hurt you, but the next time, I'm warning you, you might not get off so lightly. Now, if you'll pull yourself together, I'll take you home.'

'I'd rather die than let you!'

He only heard the defiance, the antagonism with which she hid her distress. His eyes glittered without remorse on the red blood she was attempting to rub from her chin. 'Your stubbornness might prove painful in more ways than one.'

Ignoring the veiled threat, the mocking glance he slanted at her high-heeled shoes, she turned and ran.

Physically it proved worse than she had anticipated. It was four miles home and the shoes she wore were one of the only two pairs she possessed. Bitterly she reflected how her refusal to take money from Mary for more had been rewarded. Ryan still thought of her as spoilt and useless and used every means in his power, every opportunity to remind her. If she hadn't got a lift, halfway, her heels might have been more skinned than they were.

Ryan arrived next day, as he had said he would, and was in the small office near the kitchen with Mary for what seemed like hours.

At eleven Mary popped her head around the kitchen door, ordering coffee, and when she collected it a few minutes later she said Ryan would be staying to lunch. Could Melissa have something ready for one sharp? She appeared to forget Melissa was not a good cook, nor must she realise Ryan knew it. With a mirthless grin Melissa hobbled about the untidy kitchen, ignoring Mary's advice about the steak in the larder.

The meal she produced at last was entirely out of tins—tinned soup followed by canned meat, carrots and peas. She even managed to find a tin of fruit but deliberately ignored the tub of cream in the fridge which might have improved it a little. She made no effort to tidy up the kitchen, although she felt secretly ashamed of the obvious disorder. But not even her determination to show Ryan she wasn't to be dictated to would allow her to use less than a freshly laundered cloth and spotless cutlery and glasses.

To her annoyance Ryan didn't seem to notice the unappetising menu. While he ate he talked exclusively to Mary and Lewis, but his eyes seldom left Melissa. Almost as if he were planning his next reprisal, with her in view. Melissa shivered as she placed his coffee beside him and her bare arm accidentally brushed his. She remembered the strength of that arm around her, how she hadn't been able to move. Her lips stretched in a discomfited grimace and she winced at the still unhealed cut.

After lunch Ryan asked if he might see around the greenhouses so they could decide what was most urgently needed, and, when he disappeared with Mary and Lewis, instead of washing up, Melissa took the bus into Bude. She left a note, scribbled briefly on the back of an old envelope, saying she had gone out and would be home later. She didn't apologise for leaving the dishes or that she wouldn't be around to help in the shop that afternoon. It might seem childish, but she just couldn't stay and watch Ryan lording it over everyone, suggesting they did this and that differently. No one but herself appeared to realise he wasn't giving advice. He was issuing orders which he wanted obeyed!

Bude, with its fine surfing beaches, was a popular resort, but it was still a little early in the year for the majority of tourists. She wandered along the Strand, gazing at the various shops and hotels without finding much to interest her. There was a cinema, but she had already seen the film which was showing and hadn't enjoyed it enough to see it twice. Turning away from this, she decided to go and take a look at the swimming pool at the foot of the cliffs. She might be able to hire a costume and the water would soothe her sore heels, but when she reached it her enthusiasm seemed to have gone and she returned to the Strand. She might have gone to Compass Point, from which there was a magnificent view, where she had loved to go as a child, but somehow she felt too listless to make the effort.

Her thoughts seemed too intent on wandering back to the farm, wondering what was going on, fighting a feeling of guilt. Not being nearly so indifferent to Mary's plight as she liked to pretend, she continually looked for solutions. Anything that might enable them to dispense with Ryan Trevelyan! Finding nothing feasible didn't help her feel any better, and her nerves were already frayed when she stumbled around a corner, right into him.

'Why, hello!' he exclaimed, as if as surprised as she was. 'What a coincidence!'

It was almost a minute, a strange minute, when she felt suddenly like bursting into tears, before she could pull herself together sufficiently to speak. 'How d'you mean?' Her cheeks burnt as she looked up at him and she felt herself tremble as he laid a steadying hand on her arm, something he seemed to be forever doing. 'What's a—a coincidence?'

'Bumping into you here, of course,' he explained suavely, his eyes like gimlets. 'I had to come to town on business. Naturally you had just as good a reason?'

'I had an appointment, a dental one,' she improvised wildly. He looked so thoroughly formidable, looming over her like this, she felt quite nervous of him. 'I'm on my way to catch my bus.'

'Really. A dental appointment?' One dark eyebrow disappeared against his hairline as he sarcastically surveyed the white perfection of her small, even teeth, but he didn't actually challenge her statement. The deep breath he drew was the only indication that he was having trouble with his patience. 'I'm on my way back myself, I'll give you a lift.'

She would liked to have refused but, either way, she supposed she would be in for another lecture so she might as well have it in comfort. Anyway, buses cost money.

As they drove off, contrary to her expectations, he

seemed inclined to be friendly. 'We've covered quite a bit of ground today, your mother and I. The place has great potentiality, as I suspected. A year or two of careful management should see it on its feet.'

'You're suggesting Mum isn't a good manager?'

'I think we both know that's not true, but I do have new ideas which will be profitable to incorporate. Maybe I should have said it's more important to have most of the profits ploughed back for a time—that and a lot of hard work. You're still going to pull your weight, I take it? I can rely on you?'

'Ryan,' his car was surely made for relaxation yet she couldn't seem to sit still, 'I'm sure you don't really expect I'll be able to do that?'

'You'll try?'

A quick sideways glance showed his eyes, diamondhard, but she wasn't going to be bullied into submission—or a sense of security by the false mildness of his words. He was too smooth. Earlier, yesterday, he'd used force. Now he amused himself with different tactics. She had expected him to flay her alive when he caught her in Bude, a first brief glimpse of his expression had shown he would have liked to, and secretly she had a miserable suspicion she might deserve it. She felt more than a little ashamed of herself for leaving Mary with such a lot to do. But she wasn't to be deceived by Ryan's temporary mildness of manner. It was no sure sign of a change of heart!

He repeated his question, less politely, and she said slowly, 'I might try, but I can't promise my efforts will please you. You must make allowances.'

'What for?' The sun, sinking in the west, flared straight over his dark face, 'I suggest you stop stalling and come straight out with it. You don't like work.'

'I'm bone lazy, irresponsible, callous and stupid,' she added as he paused. 'Don't worry, I have every name you ever called me imprinted forever on my heart, Mr Trevelyan!'

'Do you want to be shaken into submission again?

Is that what you're after?' He brought the car quietly to a stop beside the holding, in a corner where they couldn't be observed. Idly he switched off the engine, his eyes lingering, as he turned to her, on the red patch that marred the tempting smoothness of her mouth. Heat streamed through her. Blindly she shook her head.

'Did Ben ever kiss you?'

'No!'

Her eyes widened and he read in them the flicker of terror. His glance slipped intimately to the long, slender column of her neck, the base of her pale throat, seeing how she swallowed convulsively. 'At least I know how to scare you,' he taunted grimly. His hands going out, he gripped her shoulders, not gently. It was as if he didn't want her to forget he could be far from kind if tried too far. 'I could think of other ways of describing you. Emotional, exotic, sensuous and desirable, if you were to give yourself a chance.'

Then his hands left her to fling open the door. 'But I mustn't keep you from your work. The jobs you obviously had to leave in order to see your dentist.'

If the new plans Ryan worked out seemed both comprehensive and complicated Mary was convinced they would work. Full of enthusiasm, she appeared to have taken new heart and praised Ryan unstintingly. Even Lewis seemed more content and neither of them apparently noticed Melissa growing more and more irritated and doing less and less.

If Ryan Trevelyan had called her bluff, she decided to call his, not really believing he would do much if she didn't conform as he'd ordered. He might insist she worked her fingers to the bone, but she wouldn't do it, not for him. She wasn't ready to admit a lot of her defiance stemmed from the fact that he was still seeing Angela regularly.

In spite of her resolve to do no more than was strictly necessary, Melissa found it increasingly difficult to sit around doing nothing. She had, when she stopped to consider, never been used to doing nothing. Helen had always insisted she lead a luxuriously idle life, but she had kept her extremely busy running after her, and Melissa had rarely had a moment to spare. In the situation into which she now found herself propelled, she felt her one defence against Ryan lay in idleness, but this, she discovered, made the hours too long when your thoughts were not wholly comfortable.

Some of the young men she had met at Ryan's party rang her up and called. She had been out twice with one of them, but when she found herself studying his boyish features with increasing boredom she had known he was no answer to her problems. After the second time, when he had wanted to kiss her goodnight, rather than try and explain a natural repugnance she scarcely understood herself, she had refused to see him again. Now, she believed, word was circulating that she was frigid, but she still found it impossible to sort out the truth of her own feelings, even in her mind.

Though she doubted, if she had been given a choice, she would ever have made a career of market gardening, there were many things she enjoyed doing. When boredom got the better of her she liked helping in the greenhouses, digging her fingers into boxes of compost, tenderly pricking out the new seedlings and watching them grow. From the past she recalled helping her father do this, but since she had come home, until now, there had been little heat or compost in the greenhouses to work with. Now there was both it seemed a miracle to watch plants flourishing. It was too late for some crops this year, but this seemed all the more reason to push on with those which could be raised and forced, under heat, all the year round.

Lewis, now he had apparently lost the inclination to gamble, appeared to have discovered his old enthusiasm. Melissa didn't realise she was beginning to ask him questions and he was taking a quiet pride in being able to supply the answers, or that a new, tentative friendship was springing up between them. She hadn't been aware he could be very easy to be with, when he forgot his dry bitterness over life in general.

Most times she found him tolerant of her faults and failings, much more so, surprisingly, than Mary. He didn't mind all that much if she grew tired or despondent and took to sitting on an upturned box, watching him. She was sitting thus, one day, when Ryan arrived with Angela.

Angela stared at her as if she were a stranger. As if she hoped she would never be called on to acknowledge a young girl whose grubby hands had left soily marks on her cheeks. A girl who was too shabby in patched-up jeans to be anything else but a tramp, but who sat idly on an upturned box looking as beautiful and coolly remote as a princess!

CHAPTER SIX

WHILE Angela's curious gaze went over the newly stocked greenhouse, Ryan closed the door firmly behind them. Angela wanted to buy a pot plant. She got round to this after finishing her close surveyal of Melissa and her surroundings.

'I want one for a friend,' she explained. 'Daddy, poor darling, hasn't one to spare and I know yours are famous.' She smiled at Lewis, who immediately fell into the trap of flattery and suggested a guided tour.

'Did you have to bring her?' Melissa asked insolently, as the two moved away. 'It's sheer curiosity. She's obviously heard something. She doesn't really want to buy a plant. I've heard her father has hundreds!'

'You could wait and see.' Ryan's voice was mild but his eyes were certainly not. His glance moved coolly over her as she sat with her feet still propped on a flower pot, her arms indifferently crossed, her back against a wooden partition. 'Not quite the picture of industry, are we?'

Melissa shrugged, wondering why the sight of him always seemed enough to make her pulse race. Fright, she assured herself, fright and apprehension. He looked like a man with murder on his mind but, so far as she could see, she hadn't this time committed any great crime. It must be because she had spoken sharply of Angela, or that he hadn't been busy.

'I'm merely having a rest,' she said.

'The man I supplied to help with the extra planting doesn't remember seeing you around very early in the morning, Melissa.'

This did bring her to her feet. 'So you're having me watched? How low can you get!' She hadn't meant to sound quite so antagonistic, but she wasn't going to stand being treated like an old-time servant, without any rights!

He left her in no doubt this was exactly how he considered her. 'You take my wages, do you not?' he pointed out curtly.

'I haven't taken anything of yours,' she retorted, her eyes, thickly fringed by dark lashes, flashing green fire. 'Mum did say you'd arranged for me to have something, but I told her to keep it. I don't want a penny!'

There was a look in his eyes which filled her with terror. Tiny specks of amber glowed in his brown eyes like fire, and she could feel his hands on the soft skin of her neck, slowly squeezing the breath from her. So real was the sensation that she flinched, and he laughed softly. 'I've warned you before not to try me too far, Melissa. I know how you've scarcely done a hand's turn since I took over. You haven't worked for the wages I sent, so I'm not going to burst into tears of pity.'

'You'd better pay the extra to your spies!' Deliberately she raised her voice so that Angela came running.

'Darling,' lovingly Angela slipped her hand through Ryan's arm, 'did I hear you having a tiny argument?'

'You could have done,' he agreed, but didn't say what about. He glanced down at the plant she held. 'If you have what you want we'll go.' He patted her hand, but his gaze remained steadily on Melissa.

'I'd better call at the shop and pay Mrs Cook.'

'No need to worry about that.' He took two notes from his pocket, dropping them on one of the benches.

'Oh, thank you, darling!'

Without either of them saying goodbye, they left, Ryan carrying the orange plant. Melissa hoped the berries would all fall off!

After this, feeling unable to settle, she decided to spend the rest of the day in Bodmin. Anything to take her mind off Ryan Trevelyan! She stayed late in Bodmin, the county town of Cornwall, bumping into an old friend whom she had met again only recently. After a pleasant evening at Susan's house, Susan's brother drove her home and she agreed to have dinner with him at the end of the week. It wasn't that she really wanted to go out with Barry, it was just that she could find no ready excuse for refusing, especially when his parents had been so kind.

For some reason she felt particularly tired next morning and went off to sleep again after Mary woke her up. Usually she knew better than to close her eyes again after she was called, but she knew nothing more until she found herself lying on the floor, entangled in sheets and pillows. Thinking she had fallen out of bed in the middle of a nightmare, she panicked and tried to sit up. It was only when she raised her head she saw Ryan standing over her.

'You!' Her horrified whisper dispersed into rising anger. Just what did he think he was doing? A joke was a joke, but to tip someone out of bed like this was far from funny! It wasn't even as if he was in his own house dealing with a lazy servant. Glaring at him through the tumbled curtain of her hair, she cried, 'What right have you to come up here?'

'Blame Lewis,' he said coolly, her agitation not noticeably worrying him. 'I happened to see the roof has slates missing and he thought there was rain getting through to the attics, so, as I own the property, I decided to come and take a look—with his permission, of course. These old granite and slate farmhouses interest me, but on my way upstairs I got diverted. You shouldn't leave your door open.'

Clutching the sheet tighter across her brief nightdress, Melissa recalled her mother trying to wake her. She couldn't have closed it—not that that was any crime. She couldn't have known Ryan Trevelyan would be wandering around, poking his aristocratic nose into everything! And Lewis wouldn't have guessed she'd still be in bed.

The flicker of shame she felt at being found there was easily dismissed by fresh anger. 'Even if the door was open you had no business to come in, and even less to tip me out of bed!'

He didn't seem at all put out. He actually grinned, as if the sight of her lying there, unable to move, amused him. Then his smile faded as his eyes became hard again. 'At least you can't accuse me of setting my spies to work this morning. I can see for myself what time you get up.'

Melissa didn't mean to plead her own case, but she had started before she realised. 'I don't usually sleep until this hour. I often—I mean I used to often go riding at dawn.'

'For your own pleasure, when you had no other commitments. But you have now, to me, and I won't let you forget them.'

What was the use of trying to appeal to him, if this was what she had been doing? He was too big and hard, too supremely indifferent, looking down on her as though he would like to beat her. Why did she always seem to arouse the worst in him? Was Angela Brett the only girl he treated with gentleness?

Conscious that nothing she could say was going to help, she exclaimed tensely, 'You've made your point. Now, if you're satisfied, will you just go!'

He smiled at her sleep and temper-flushed face mockingly. 'I didn't say I was satisfied. It's ten o'clock. Your mother is fully occupied in the shop and Lewis is busy in the gardens. It's not often I have you completely at my mercy.'

'Please!' She was reduced to pleading, but suddenly her pride was not so important. The mattress, tipped off the bed, was like a wall on one side and Ryan was at the other. She was imprisoned and dared not move as she had so little on. He wasn't lecherous—on her travels with Helen she had seen so much of this she was able to judge—but he knew she hated being touched and had chosen to punish her apparent laziness with indirect hints calculated to flood her with terror.

For all she strove to stay cool she found her common sense slipping and allowed a mild hysteria to take over when coolness might have done more for her. Suddenly, still clutching the sheet, she tried to scramble up, but he caught her, almost before she was on her feet. Trying to fight him loosened her grip on the sheet, which fell from her, exposing her near-to-nothing nightdress to his interested glance.

That was all he did, glance at her briefly, but, hot all over, Melissa felt he had seen everything. 'Let me go!' she cried.

'When I'm ready.' His arm around her tightened ruthlessly as he held her trembling body to him and, without mercy, grasped a handful of hair. As he jerked her head back, her mouth opened in wild protest, but before the scream in her throat could escape his mouth was on hers.

Numbly she tried to move, but he held her still and her blood began to race, licking through her veins like a fire out of control. He had a strength she deplored, if some part of her couldn't seem to resist it. Yet for all the heat and excitement he aroused, fear was stronger. Her mind fought and triumphed over traitorous senses, but it wasn't easy to push him away. His hand, entangled in her hair, held her head in a vice. Try as she might she couldn't escape him as he plundered the soft, shaken warmth of her mouth until she felt like fainting.

At last, slowly, his warm breath brushed her throat as he allowed her to slip from his arms. 'Right,' he said, his voice deep and hard, so that she almost recoiled from him, 'that might just about make up for lost time—the time you owe me.'

'Owe you?' Melissa didn't feel the tears streaming down her burning cheeks. 'I don't owe you anything!'

'Merely the word you gave.'

'I was entitled to change my mind.'

'Not regarding the bargain we made.'

'I'll please myself about that!' The sob she gave was born of temper and his mouth thinned.

'Not with me, you won't,' his anger appeared to be mounting as steadily as her own, only where hers sprang from fright, his was based on ice.

She wanted to hit out at him, do him some injury, anything to release the peculiar violence which seemed to have mounted within her, but she remembered how ineffectual it was to try and hurt him this way. If she tried to slap his face he would see her hand coming a mile off, and the only thing to hurl was a pillow.

There were only words left. In the devastation of her mind she found a few with suitable defiance. 'You can't physically make me dance to your tune and I know you care too much for your reputation as an exemplary landlord to throw us out. What would darling Angela think? She may not like me, but she might like even less to hear you're capable of such measures.'

Whatever Melissa had hoped for, other than to be rid of him, she wasn't prepared for his extreme fury. 'Before I'm finished with you,' he retorted grimly, 'you'll rue the day you dared speak her name.' His eyes fell indifferently on her tears, the haunted whiteness of her face as his voice slaughtered her, 'I'm warning you, Melissa, warning you for the last time. I'll give you one more week to reform—or else!'

That week was the longest—and the shortest— Melissa had ever lived through. She didn't know where she got the courage to continue defying him, but continue she did. Perhaps it was an inherent stubbornness, combined with hurt pride and a sore heart. A dark bitterness came over her whenever she thought of how he defended Angela. Added to this was an almost morbid curiosity to see if he really would do anything, after a week, as he threatened.

Something drove her on. Nothing explainable, but not even the sight of Mary and Lewis, obviously happier, seemed able to divert her from acting as she did. She couldn't really believe she was imperilling their future. If she was then she might have reason to be ashamed, but there was nothing she could do about it.

In some strange way she felt her feet were set on a course from which there was no turning back, and on one over which she had no control.

She was rarely at the holding. She spent most of the week with Barry, leaving her work to be done by the extra help Ryan supplied. She noticed this had been increased to two men and that a woman arrived each morning to help her mother. These people, she had little doubt, would acquaint Ryan with most of her movements. She was even foolish enough to lift her chin and smile at him as she and Barry passed him in Bodmin one day, but she had to forgo his reactions as her courage wouldn't take her as far as the smouldering coldness of his eyes.

Yet the following Tuesday, when a letter arrived from his solicitor, she almost broke down and wept, and it only made her feel much worse that neither Mary or Lewis reproached her.

Mary's face was white as she passed the brief missive on to Lewis, as they sat around the breakfast table, and turned unseeing eyes towards Melissa. 'Ryan's solicitor,' she offered needlessly. 'He's been asked to inform us that Ryan considers he's made a mistake and feels it better to admit it before things go any further. He would naturally like us out of here as soon as possible, and awaits our comments.'

'A formal notice,' Lewis shrugged. 'Well, old girl, we seem finally to have come to the end of the road. We can't honourably fight this!'

'But why?' Mary's face was pathetic in its grey anxiousness. 'Everything seemed to be working all right. It's just been five weeks, but I'd never have believed we'd make such progress. People have remarked on it. Already we're selling more to the caravans along the road, and to passing motorists. Ryan even said himself . . .'

Her voice trailed off, as if she found it difficult to go on, and Melissa, trying desperately to stem her conscience, cried, 'Are you sure he means it, Mum?'

'If you're in any doubt, read that.' Lewis flicked her the letter, watching as she quickly read it.

There was something so final about it, the words seemed to dance before her eyes. Inside she felt cold, horribly cold all over, although the morning was warm. 'Don't you think we should wait a few days? Even now he could be regretting. Maybe if we took no notice...?'

'No!' Mary swiftly regained control of herself. Melissa saw her hands were shaking as she poured a second cup of tea, but otherwise she seemed calm. It was only when she couldn't lift the cup to her lips that Melissa realised her mother scarcely knew what she was doing.

'Mum?' she entreated, guilt tearing at her, a kind of frantic remorse.

'Don't worry,' Mary took a deep breath, 'I'm all right now. I'll ring Ryan's solicitor at once, although, as it's only after eight, I don't suppose he'll be in his office yet. I'd better leave it until around ten-thirty as,' she picked up the letter, peering at it closely, 'I see he isn't in his office until ten. Maybe Ryan will let us stay on in the house a little longer, until we find something else. But go we must! No one could have been kinder than Ryan Trevelyan and I know he wouldn't have done this without a very good reason. I do have some pride left.'

She might! Melissa felt so sick it was difficult to speak. Mary was entitled to and could keep her pride, but Melissa couldn't share any such privilege. Nor, she admitted, did she deserve to. Defying Ryan Trevelyan had become a daring game, useless and childishly foolish. However justified she had imagined it to be it hadn't been sufficient reason to make Mary and Lewis suffer like this.

What a fool she had been to think Ryan wouldn't have the nerve to do anything! First and foremost he was a business man and this holding would be but a drop in the ocean of his various interests. He would as easily brush it aside and forget it as he would an irritating fly.

For Mary's sake she must go and plead with him—if there was still time. Mary and Lewis might have their suspicions, probably would have when they got round to thinking about it, but they couldn't know for certain what lay behind the shattering news of the morning. Yet it wasn't her own part in what had happened which drove her to Poldary a few minutes later, it was the look of absolute despair on Mary's face. Alone, Melissa told herself, she could have lived without seeing Ryan almost every day. She didn't feel any different towards him, but she knew, quite suddenly, she would never be completely happy again if Mary lost the farm. Not through her!

She was in such a hurry she didn't consider it might have made a more humble impression if she had gone to the back door. It wasn't nine o'clock and she was praying so feverishly that Ryan hadn't gone out yet, she was ringing wildly at the front before she realised.

When Mrs Barr came to the door she looked surprised to see her and no more welcoming than she had done the last time Melissa called.

When Melissa asked, she said she was sorry Mr Trevelyan wasn't in, and, when Melissa made no move to leave, enquired politely if she could help.

'No—I mean, yes,' Melissa gasped. 'If you could tell me where he's gone?' She didn't care about Mrs Barr's suspicious glance; it was imperative she found him.

'I think he might have gone for the day,' Mrs Barr replied woodenly.

'Won't you please tell me where?' Her voice carried a mixture of pleading and impatience. 'I must know where to find him!'

'Right here!' Ryan's two words hit her sharply, jerking her attention from Mrs Barr. He was walking across the hall; she doubted if he had been out at all as he carried what appeared to be the morning's mail in his hand, and his expression was as cold as his house-keeper's.

'Thank you, Mrs Barr,' he drawled, 'I'll see to Miss Grant, although I can only give her a minute. I've too busy a day in front of me to bother myself over triviali-ties.'

Melissa guessed he had spoken with the deliberate intention of humiliating her and, judging from Mrs Barr's departing face, the snub was being memorised to be related to Angela Brett. Without looking at Melissa again Ryan turned and strode into the sitting room where she recalled him having tea with Angela, but this scarcely registered as she ran quickly after him, as if afraid he might disappear.

'Ryan!' As he came to a halt, facing her abruptly, words failed her. She hadn't anything rehearsed; so intent had she been on getting here she had no idea what she was going to say. Somehow she had to get Ryan to change his mind about the holding before ten o'clock, but she hadn't an inkling how to set about it. Dazed, she watched as he came back to slam the door behind her, hoping the force he used didn't altogether express his feelings.

'Ryan——' She swivelled uncertainly, trying to find even a flicker of warmth in his face, trembling to see him so unyielding. 'Ryan, Mum had a letter this morn-ing from your solicitor. You—you don't really mean it?'

'If you're trying to ask if I'm serious about giving your mother notice to quit, then indeed I am.'

Her face slowly paling, she stared at him aghast. A dreadful conviction hit her that she was wasting her time. Ryan was withdrawn, aloof, his features might have been chiselled from stone, and he looked at Melissa in her shabby clothes with distinct contempt. She knew a fleeting if hopeless regret that she hadn't worn something smarter. She might have found some-thing if she'd tried, and it might have helped. Patched jeans and a worn tee-shirt never charmed a man, but when her eyes met his, she realised it wouldn't have made any difference if she'd arrived in mink.

'Ryan,' she was pleading now, 'you can't do it. If you'd seen Mum's face——!'

'You ought to have thought of that sooner,' he broke in.

God, he was like steel! Did he want her to beg? Her face flushed with resentment, then, remembering just what such an attitude had achieved, she tried desperately to change it. Not that she had to try very hard. Suddenly she seemed hit by a wall of sheer terror, a wholly consuming apprehension which took her impetuously over the space between them until she was grasping his arm, gazing up into his face.

Her own was eloquent of the fear rushing through her, brilliant with the shimmer of tears in her eyes. 'I'm sorry, Ryan. I know it's all my fault, but I don't know what got into me. I promise I'll work as hard as you like in future, if only you'll give me another chance. I'll slave, do anything you want me to, if only you'll ring Mum and tell her you've had second thoughts about turning her out.'

'How very moving!' His smile was completely mirthless, as he bent his dark head and stared at her. 'The tempestuous Miss Grant, who can't bear a man near her, forced to come a-begging. I'm just waiting for you to go down on your knees. I'm no God but, by heaven, I'd like to see it!'

Her eyes wide in her anguished face, Melissa could think of nothing else but to do as he asked. With a low, tormented cry she sank to the floor, only to be immediately hauled up again by the scruff of her neck. Hauled up, she decided thankfully, because he couldn't bear to actually see her in such a lowly position. But her small triumph was shortlived. Without a word he yanked her across his knee to receive the full force of his hand, not once but several times, until she cried out in pain. Then she was thrust to her feet where he shook her forcibly until she was sobbing blindly. Not hurt so much as humiliated, she hoped wildly that he felt better. But no sooner had the thought entered her head than she found herself dragged against him, his mouth dealing mercilessly with the quivering softness of hers, inflicting further punishment.

Almost reeling with shock, she was unable to move. Both the force of his mouth and lean hands were insulting, but strangely she knew none of her usual revulsion. The blood pounded in her ears, her pulse raced, and she was lost in a quickening of desire which made her cling to him. A wide elation filled her and her body became pliant, incredibly soft against the rugged strength of his.

Suddenly he jerked his head back, as if he saw warning lights she couldn't, and some of his savagery appeared to diminish as he saw how white she was. He pushed her from him into a chair and turned his back while he poured himself a double whisky.

'I'm not offering you one,' he said. 'I happen to remember what happened last time.'

Aching all over, Melissa would have welcomed something, anything to stop her shaking, to steady her nerves. She wondered if he usually downed double whiskies at this time of the morning. His second lot was almost thrown down, but she dared not comment. After the ordeal she had just come through—which she didn't think she wholly deserved—she felt too distraught to even open her mouth and comment on the weather. And this was only the beginning. He hadn't yet promised her anything, and the only certainty in her mind was one of failure.

He came at last and sat opposite her, apparently forgetting he had promised her only a minute. His eyes took in her forlorn appearance, but there was a sneer, not an apology, on his lips. 'We'll begin at the beginning,' his voice was laced with sarcasm. 'Your mother has a letter from Courtney, Brown and Fielding and you take straight off up here?'

Melissa chose her words with great care, feeling she

was walking through a minefield. 'I wasn't sure if I was responsible for you sending it. The only way I could find out was to come and ask. I could have phoned, but Mum doesn't know, you see, about—about ...'

'About what's been going on,' he finished derisively for her.

'If you like,' she breathed nervously.

'If I like? Oh, what the hell!' He rose, as if to seek another drink, then visibly restrained himself. A hint of violence returned to his face, enough to make her shake again and wonder what was coming. 'I warned you last week and since then you've gone on exactly as before, going into town each day, never doing any work. You've spent most of your time playing around with Barry Ward. I saw you in Bodmin.'

'I remember.'

'For a girl who doesn't like men you have quite a collection. Did you expect me to stand by while you played around—slept around too, most probably, if your exhaustion in the mornings is anything to go by!'

She had never thought it would be so hard to bite her lip, to endure such castigation without retaliation. For that last accusation, even after what she had endured, she would liked to have slapped his sneering face, but she knew when she was beaten. The most she dared was a small protest, which she couldn't see how he could object to. 'I don't sleep around.'

'Evidence weighs heavily.'

'Against my word, you mean?'

'Precisely.' His stare was frosty. 'I've learnt not to rely on that. Can you blame me?'

Not able to deny it, Melissa shook her head unhappily. 'With such an opinion of me I can't see how I can be so important, regarding the holding. Mum and Lewis are doing everything they can. Mum's been thrilled by the way things are going.'

'I'm beginning to think you're right,' he shrugged cynically. 'Why should I allow someone to get under

my skin to such an extent? Things escalated and, in
retrospect, it seems rather crazy that I ever came to par-
ticipate in such a scheme. However, I've come to my
senses in time and the sooner I put things right the
better.'

'But you can't back out now!' Melissa leant forward
in her chair, her eyes darkening with an intensity of
feeling. 'Please, Ryan, I'm ready to promise—almost
anything!'

His attention was held for a calculating moment, but
his voice, when he went on, was still curt. 'Listen to
me, Melissa, before making any rash promises. Your
parents are more heavily in debt than you realise. I
wasn't unsympathetic as I know the whole story and
was willing to give them time. Then, as they obviously
couldn't find a solution on their own, I provided what
I thought was an honourable, face-saving way out, but
it depended on everybody. Already I've put in quite a
lot of capital. To me it's never been the idle game you
consider it to be, and unless you're prepared to put all
you've got into it——'

As he paused, unable to wait, she whispered, 'Does
that mean you've relented? You'll give me another
chance?'

The telephone rang, interrupting. He snatched the
receiver. 'Trevelyan here.' Then, 'Yes. Just give me five
minutes.'

Putting the instrument back in its cradle, he spoke
to Melissa. 'I'm not willing to make any immediate de-
cisions. I'd like you to come back this evening to discuss this properly. There's a chap in my office waiting
to see me. That was my agent, so I really can't spare
you any more time just now.'

'And if I do?'

'Then I'll ring your mother and tell her not to do
anything until she hears from me, but I'm warning
you, Melissa, you'd better think about everything carefully. No one makes a fool of me twice.'

'I'll do that, and I'll be here,' she promised, having

the awful sensation of being suspended halfway
through an ordeal.

He picked up the telephone again and dialled. She
heard him speaking to Mary as if from a distance. She
watched his hands and strongly set mouth move, feeling she was hovering weightlessly in outer space, unable to find a firm footing. It was a faint noise at the
door as Ryan finished the call that jerked her back to
reality. It was like the squeak of a loose floorboard
which, but for a moment's complete silence, might
never have been heard.

Ryan was aware of something, too, as his glance
swivelled downwards and he frowned. 'Old houses
creak.'

As she agreed, not really caring, his nod was one of
dismissal. 'I'll see you later. It all depends on you.'

On such a cryptic remark, as she sped back to the
holding, she could only dwell with misgiving.

'Where have you been!' asked Mary.

'I was going out,' Melissa had to think of an excuse
quickly, 'then I changed my mind. I suppose I'm not in
the mood, considering what's happened.'

Mary was too excited to comment. 'You'll never
guess who rang?'

'I ...'

'Ryan,' Melissa's brief hesitation wasn't noticed, but
Mary's jubilance was tinged with apprehension. 'He
doesn't want me to ring his solicitor. He wants me to
wait until the morning. Oh, Melissa,' her words
jumbled, 'I may be wrong, but I'm hoping he's changed
his mind.'

'Quite probably.'

Mary's mouth twisted unhappily. 'I don't know how
I'm going to get through today, though. You don't
think he would keep me in suspense like this unless
he'd had second thoughts?'

'I couldn't honestly say, Mum. Perhaps it might be
wiser not to build up your hopes too far. We must just

hope for the best. I can't say I like the situation any more than you do.'

'I know.'

Feeling a hypocrite, Melissa looked at Mary's ravaged face. This, she realised, was all part of Ryan's revenge. She must spend endless hours contemplating her mother's needless suffering, knowing herself responsible.

'Look, Mum,' she banged shut the car door, wishing it could have been on Ryan's head, 'supposing you go and make yourself a cup of coffee while I open the shop? Maybe if I'm where Mr Trevelyan can actually see me working it might help.'

Like Mary she began to believe the day would never end. Not even the considerable amount of work she managed to get through made the hours go faster. At seven she went upstairs for a bath. Parts of her still ached from Ryan's rough handling and she suspected only hot water might soothe them. She felt nervous, tensed up, afraid if he tried the same tactics this evening she might not be able to hide the hate she felt for him. Whatever happened he must never guess. If he did, she suspected Mary could say goodbye to the holding for ever!

Discarding her jeans, in an effort to make a good impression, she wore a calf-length skirt and top she had made herself from a piece of silky material she had found in an old trunk in her room. Mary hadn't been able to remember where it had come from and thought it must have been there for years. They had both been amused over the small, muted print which, surprisingly enough, was the height of fashion again. Fortunately the moths hadn't been hungry!

Melissa was, for all her faults, extremely handy with her needle. The outfit looked good. The skirt fell in soft folds, the top was brief but ideal for such a warm evening. Thinking it would all help, she used a lot of make-up and let her hair fall siren-like over her shoulders. If she had to crawl at least she would do it gracefully. Even Angela Brett might be hard put to it to look so charming in spite of her expensive clothes.

'I'm going out for a while.' She looked in on Mary and Lewis finishing supper.

'Will you be late?' Mary's frown was motherish. 'You've been so busy today.'

'I don't think so.' Melissa smiled with an effort and closed the kitchen door. She sensed Mary would liked to have known where she was going but, for once, it might be kinder not to tell her.

The car went smoothly. She had half hoped it might break down, but it had gone well since Ryan had seen to having it repaired. Still, she wasn't one for putting off. If she had to see Ryan and hear the worst she might as well get it over. It was such a pleasant evening she could think of nicer things she would rather have done, but she could never hope to enjoy herself until this was settled.

Practising the docile demeanour she had decided on, she drove quietly around to the rear door of Poldary. There, just as quietly, she left the car and walking over the flagstone knocked sedately. This might impress Mrs Barr more favourably than her wild ringing of the morning.

No one came. She knocked again, this time a little louder, but with the same result. Mrs Barr was probably upstairs or at the front of the house. Forgetting the favourable impression she hoped to make, Melissa opened the door and went in. Quickly she walked along the back passage into the kitchen.

'Mrs Barr,' she began sharply, only to be brought up short when confronted by Ryan. In the diffused light from the westering sun she had made a mistake. He was sitting at the table, the remains of a meal and bottle of wine before him. As he glanced towards her his hand halted abruptly on its way towards his half empty glass.

'Do you always barge straight in?' he asked curtly, as she stared at him in startled surprise.

'No. No, of course not.' She was too discouraged by

his sombre face to speak anything but the truth.

Grimly he replied. 'In your circumstances wouldn't it have been better to knock and wait until you were asked?'

CHAPTER SEVEN

IT wasn't an auspicious beginning. Clearly Ryan was not impressed. 'I did knock!' My knees still are, she almost added, suppressing a mirthless giggle. 'You don't have to look as if you'd resort to violence again.'

'Don't you ever learn?' His gaze was long and level as he hacked himself a piece of cheese. 'I'll tell you something. If you don't take that silly grin off your face, I might.'

'I'm not laughing,' she gulped, adding another silent comment—you great bully! He knew she was down and he was going to make the most of it. She must be ready to bow and scrape. This she had been prepared for, but it was infuriating to know it might make little difference in the end. Uneasily she was aware that a man didn't usually instruct his solicitor until he was very sure of what he was doing. There was little real likelihood that he would change his mind. Yet she must try. 'I'm sorry,' she said dully, trying to make a start.

'I'm pleased to hear it.' He studied her with cold insolence, making no attempt to rise to his feet, nor did he invite her to sit down. A pity her name wasn't Angela, Melissa thought angrily.

Turning her betraying eyes from his narrowed ones, she looked around for Mrs Barr. Ryan was picnicking in the kitchen, so she must be out, but one never knew. 'I expected to see your housekeeper,' she offered, by way of explanation. 'She's usually here?'

'She's away on her annual vacation. Gone to visit her sister for a week.'

'Oh.' Melissa didn't know whether to be pleased or sorry. She could do without Mrs Barr's disapproving glances, but she did feel sort of happier when she was in the house.

'She was away the first time you were here,' he noted briefly, 'and again you're not sure whether to be grateful or just plain scared she isn't here to protect you.'

Melissa saw no point in denying this. 'You think a lot of her, don't you? And she likes Angela.'

'I'll not bother to sort that out.'

She tried again. 'Do you have to look after yourself while Mrs Barr is away?'

'I manage quite well on my own. My manager's wife will look in and invite me to dinner. If I'm nice to her she might even tidy up a bit and wash my dishes. Otherwise I just dump the lot in that huge dishwasher behind you. Of course, as you so deviously suggest, there's always Angela.'

There would be! Dismally Melissa sat down at the other side of the table.

'Again without waiting to be asked!'

'Whatever do you—oh, I see!' Her cheeks scarlet, she jumped to her feet. If the crawling had to begin here, she might as well comply.

'For God's sake sit down!'

'I'm sorry.' She concentrated on the right degree of servility.

'Well, well!' he drawled mockingly. 'I was going to offer you humble pie, but I didn't think you would eat it.'

His voice held not a scrap of humour and she snatched back a returning volley of words from off the end of her tongue. Silence could be painful but wiser.

'Would you like some cheese?' Idly he pushed it towards her, contemplating her hot face.

'I'm not hungry,' which wasn't wholly true as she had skipped supper, rather than share it with Mary and Lewis, rather than subject herself to the possibility of having to be too evasive about her night out.

'Coffee, then?'

'Yes. But,' she said tightly, 'you don't have to keep on being polite. Wouldn't it be better to say what you're obviously going to say, and I went? Then you'd be free to enjoy your evening.'

He looked at her steadily. 'I believe I asked you here to hear what you have to say. Knowing this I didn't plan to enjoy my evening, but I do like my dinner in peace. Now, how about coffee?'

Giving in dumbly, she nodded, 'Thank you. Shall I pour it out?'

'It's not made yet. I seem to remember it's one of the few things you're good at.'

Glad to have a reprieve, if only a brief one, from this verbal battle, she nodded again and went over to the percolator. As long as she wasn't deceived by this short respite there could be no harm in sharing coffee with him. He looked easy and relaxed, lounging in his chair, but she must remember predators almost always took their time.

'Isn't it ready yet?' He came over to where she stood, giving the percolator a slow turn before slanting a cool look at her. 'So you came to repent your sins?'

'You're not a god.'

'No. Neither am I as willing to forgive you.'

What had happened to his truce? He should have stated its brevity! Quickly she lowered her lashes to hide her resentment. He wanted her to beg and was going to see she did! One day she would know the luxury of revenge. One day she would make him suffer! Now the only crumb of comfort she could find was in holding such a resolution in front of her, like a flag of defiance!

Quickly she retorted, 'I'm not so concerned about myself. It's Lewis and Mary.'

He laughed, his eyes glinting. 'You could be concerned about yourself, before I'm finished with you.' Placing his hands at either side of her, as she stood against the bench, he stared down at her. 'Just what did you hope to gain tonight, coming here, dressed and made up like this?'

'I made this outfit myself.'

'I'm astonished, I really am.' His eyes, still glinting, wandered slowly over the brief top to halt contemplatively on the high, tense curves of her figure, as if he realised she scarcely dared breathe. She could feel the warmth of his thighs against hers, his breath stirring her hair, and knew instinctively that his closeness wasn't accidental. She sensed his movements were deliberate, devised to frighten her, and was determined to show him she didn't scare easily. Not unless a man tried to kiss her.

It was only as her glance wandered to the half-open front of his shirt that she felt startled. She was so near she was able to see the rise and fall of his broad chest beneath the hair-roughened skin, and she quivered. With her two hands she groped for and found the rounded edge of the wood behind her and gripped tight. She was aware of the most disturbing sensations as the desire which made her fingers want to touch him seemed to travel up her arms and consume her whole body.

Above her Ryan's face went still, his mouth tightening as he reached out to switch off the percolator. 'How badly do you want me to rescind that note your mother received, Melissa?'

Melissa tried to speak evenly, to ignore the peculiar excitement within her, her racing pulse. Carefully she strove to choose her words. 'I'm willing to beg you to cancel it.'

Not easily fooled, he taunted, 'How would you set about that?'

'I'm not sure.' She didn't want to look at him and twisted her head. 'You said we would talk.'

'You asked if I would talk,' he corrected. 'You said you wouldn't—or implied you wouldn't, object to anything I might suggest if I gave you another chance at the farm.'

Feeling trapped, she saw herself reflected in the darkness of his mocking eyes. 'If you'd just let me sit down for a minute,' she muttered desperately, 'I'll consider anything you want.'

But Ryan didn't immediately comply. With a faint smile his hands went to her waist, pulling her against him, the buckle of his pants hurting her stomach as he lowered his head. His mouth touched the frantic pulse at the base of her throat briefly, then her cheek. In trying to push him away her own mouth came under his and he crushed her lips softly until her head whirled and she was clinging to him. Then, as suddenly as he had taken her, he let her go. 'Perhaps we'd better have our coffee—and talk, before it goes cold?'

While he poured coffee she watched him furtively, her usual self-confidence completely shaken. What did he expect from her? If the last few minutes had been meant as a hint, how far did he expect her to go? Fright quickened her pulse, ebbed through her stomach, taking the strength from her legs. Surely he wasn't going to demand that she sleep with him, or something like that, before he would promise to tear up that note? Her senses swam and her breath came quickly as she tried to think rationally. No, her tremors subsiding, Melissa assured herself more sensibly, he had only been teasing—trying to frighten her.

Her composure returning, she almost managed to smile as she drank her coffee. Ryan sat on the edge of the table watching her, his silence so misleading she started when he spoke. 'If I do give you another chance, I suppose you're going to renew your promise to work hard?'

'Yes,' she dropped her head so he wouldn't see her relief that this was all he required. 'I know I promised that before, but this time I really mean it. I realise I couldn't expect you to overlook the same thing twice, but if you'd only forgive me ...'

'It's a matter of business,' his hardness swept aside any illusion it could be anything else. 'Nothing so personal as forgiveness comes into it.'

'Then wouldn't you be better off without me?' she asked quickly.

'Melissa!' he sighed constrictively. 'Haven't we been through all this before? Only if you swear to co-operate, not run away, will I consider it!'

With Mary's suffering face in mind, Melissa drew a deep breath. 'I'll do it for Mum's sake.'

'Not mine?'

He was tripping her with words and she was still so confused from being in his arms she wasn't sure whether to say yes or no. 'You must realise I'm doing it for Mum,' she answered stiffly, 'and Lewis.'

Ryan's cup hit its saucer. 'Suppose I agree to starting again, don't you think I deserve something?'

'Of course,' she forced a warmer note into her voice, 'you'll have my gratitude.'

'I'd get fat on that!' Despite the irony in his tones there was a look in his eyes which leapt Melissa's heart to her throat.

'What more can I say?' She popped another spoonful of sugar into her last drain of coffee and took a quick gulp.

His mouth twisted briefly. 'It's up to you to think that one out.'

Think? What more could she think of? She glanced at him quickly again, her lashes fluttering. There was a frightening alertness in the way he was looking at her. His glance went over her face, the rich luxuriance of her hair, the soft green of her eyes. He didn't stop there. His glance travelled down her slender neck, to the shadowed hollow between her breasts, to which the silk of her top clung seductively, then on to the narrow waist and long slim legs before reversing upwards again.

The sensation she had felt before began to stir, building up to a frightening turbulence everywhere his eyes touched. Scarcely knowing what she was doing, Melissa began very carefully easing herself from her chair, measuring the distance to the door in her mind's eye while wondering if she could move as swiftly as she wanted to.

'Melissa!' She wasn't aware he moved too, until he was suddenly between herself and the door, making immediate escape impossible. His voice came deceptively low. 'Were you going somewhere?'

'I was thinking of going home.' She tried to speak calmly as his hands gripped her elbows, bringing her to an abrupt halt.

'I hoped you would stay.' He was very close, his breath against her face. 'Remember I haven't promised anything yet.'

Melissa licked her lips tremulously. Her mind seemed to be separating from her body and she found herself leaning weakly against him, not wanting to move. 'I thought you had?' she managed.

'Then you were mistaken,' he murmured, his arms going right around her, his mouth against her ear. 'You take too much for granted. Because I don't bawl you out you think you've won the day.'

'I don't.' The unhurried movement of his mouth teasing her ear and cheek made her melt inside. Her heart began to race as he turned her head a little and kissed her lips.

At once some of her old horror returned, and with it her strength, an ability to fight. It wasn't diplomatic to fight, not with so much at stake, but she couldn't help it. She wasn't strong enough but, for a brief moment when she took him by surprise, she thought she was winning.

Panting, she realised that though she had managed to free her mouth, he still held her. His mocking laughter froze her.

'You can struggle all you will, but if you're sensible you won't.'

'What is it you really want, Ryan?'

'Nothing you don't want to give willingly,' he taunted.

It was then she did the wrong thing. Lifting a sandalled foot, she kicked him, as she had done once before, and something within him exploded to a contradictory but somehow dreadful stillness.

'A habit of yours?'

'You scare me!'

The glint in his eyes didn't lessen, nor did he release her. 'Men seem to, when they get too close,' he said coolly. 'I'm not going to take it too personally. Wouldn't you like to talk about it? While kicking and screaming might relieve your immediate feelings they won't remove the root cause.'

Her heart began pounding frantically at her ribs again, as his heavily muscled limbs pinned her to the bench and she watched his mouth in a kind of panicky fascination.

'I've told you, I just don't like being kissed.'

'If you really don't it's nothing to joke about.'

She glanced up but found herself unable to meet his calculating gaze. 'I'm glad you realise.'

'On the other hand,' he suggested, his fingers playing gently with her chin, 'you might if you gave yourself a chance. Is it only kisses you reject? Have you ever slept with a man?'

'Of course not!' She began to tremble violently as his eyebrows arched mockingly at her rigid denial.

'Why so emphatic? You might easily have done.'

'Well, I haven't. Although why I'm telling you ...'

His voice was oddly persuasive. 'If you had it's nothing to be exactly ashamed of. I'm no fool. At some time you've had a fright?'

'No——' she still couldn't tell him.

'Well then,' he muttered, brushing his lips briefly across hers again, 'it must be something inside you. Something you were born with which needs to be put right.'

She stared at his strong throat, which was just about as distracting as looking into his eyes. 'I think we should forget all this and resume our discussion about the holding.'

'No,' his hand thrust through her hair, holding her still, 'I want to make love to you. I want to show you there's nothing so terrible about being kissed.' His voice roughened. 'Persevere and I think you'll even come to like it.'

'Please, Ryan!'

But her frantic protest was lost against his mouth, as it closed gently over her own, as if he really wanted to soothe away her fears. For a moment she tried to resist, but he deepened the pressure again and again, each time she tried to escape him until she realised he wasn't going to let her go. It was as if he was relying on the magnetism between them, the age-old, primeval rapport, which he understood if she did not, to work its infallible magic.

As his hard, arousing kiss seared through her and his arms crushed her against the whipcord strength of his body a sudden rush of desire forced aside her former fears. His lips were hot and searching and she became totally confused, lost in a world where only sensation mattered and her inhibitions steadily disappeared beneath his expertise.

Her mouth trembled, her lips parting involuntarily under his as he pushed her brief top out of the way. Lightly his hands moved over her shoulders to her back, his fingers tracing the bones of her spine right down to the cleft below her narrow waist. Never before had she known such sensations existed as those which rippled through her at his touch. She sagged against him, all the resistance knocked out of her, as his hands came slowly across her rib-cage to find her bare breasts. He stroked them gently until wave after wave of heart-stopping excitement began hitting her and she scarcely dared breathe for fear he might stop.

Her arms found their way around his neck as she was unable to disguise her own needs and desires. Murmuring his name again and again, she felt the warmth of him as his arms tightened to bring her almost savagely against the roughness of his chest. She was aware of a new urgency in his mouth, of an unexpected surge of passion to which she found herself responding eagerly. Then she couldn't speak again until he let her.

At last he lifted his head just a fraction. 'Melissa,' he groaned against her mouth, 'I want you. You say you've never belonged to a man before. Is that really true?'

As he held her slightly away from him she could see the dampness of perspiration on his face. She didn't want to look at him, but he made her.

'Melissa,' he tilted her chin up, 'I asked you a question.'

'Yes,' she quivered beneath his hard satisfaction, 'I've already told you I've never slept with a man!'

'I want you,' he repeated. 'You're lovely, enticing, responsive—for all you pretend to be otherwise. I want to make love to you until you don't care what I do to you, or what you're doing.' The thickness of his voice blurred in her ears as, once more, he pulled her to him, his hand over her hips holding her tightly, making her aware, even in her innocence, of his overwhelming need of her.

As his mouth opened over hers, instinctively she knew what he wanted, what he intended ruthlessly to take unless she made some effort to stop him. Fiercely she wanted to give in to him, to her clamouring senses, but while the same longing tormented her a tiny fraction of her mind protested. 'No, Ryan. Let me go!' she gasped.

Harshly he brushed aside her feeble cry, feeling how, in spite of her reluctance, her body still clung helplessly to his. 'Do you want to go upstairs? I don't mind the kitchen floor——'

Suddenly she felt herself surrendering, no shame touching her any more as she soared tremulously above it. 'I don't care, darling. Either way——'

'Ryan?'

Angela Brett's shrill call was shattering, but no more so than her presence when, a minute or two later, she

burst in on them. There was only time to move frac-
tionally apart. Melissa scarcely had a moment to pull
herself together, to straighten her crumpled top, or
Ryan to rub the betraying lipstick from off his mouth.

It was perhaps fortunate that one of the dogs chose
to rush wildly in between Angela's legs. As she strove
angrily to disentangle herself, Ryan buttoned up his
shirt. As Melissa left his side she pretended not to hear
what he muttered tersely, half under his breath, as a
wave of shame engulfed her as surely as passion had
almost done.

'I must be going,' she whispered, her voice weak,
feeling, for all her dislike of Angela, happier than
Ryan that she had arrived. She kept her eyes averted
from Ryan. She remembered she must speak to him
before she left, but she didn't want to look at him. That
she found impossible, with her pulses still racing so
unevenly.

Angela, regaining her balance, glanced at Melissa
with dislike and a trace of suspicion before turning to
Ryan. 'I was looking for you. I didn't know you had
company, but I expect it's all right if Miss Grant is just
leaving.' When no one replied, she went on, 'As Mrs
Barr is away, Ryan, I thought you'd need someone to
cook your dinner. I'd have been here earlier, but we
had company and I couldn't get away.'

Liar, thought Melissa, her gratitude fading. Angela
had craftily chosen the gloaming hours, the twilight
ones, no doubt hoping to catch Ryan in a softer mood.

'I've already eaten,' she heard Ryan reply, and
watched as he tore a sheet of soft kitchen paper, carelessly rubbing his mouth. As he tossed it into the stove,
Angela smiled brightly.

'Oh, I see. You've just finished.'

'Actually,' he said deliberately, his mocking glance
flicking to Melissa, 'I'd only just got started.'

'Oh, what a shame!' Angela cast another hostile
glance at Melissa. 'Never mind, I can always make you
a snack later on.' Mistaking Melissa's flaming cheeks for

guilt, she sniffed, 'I expect it's cold now, what you were having?'

'I'm afraid you could be right.'

As Ryan spoke the slight grin on his face was for Melissa alone, and she understood what he hinted at, which fortunately Angela didn't. Or if she did she chose to ignore it. If Ryan liked to amuse himself occasionally with one of his workers she was willing to turn a blind eye—always providing he wasn't seriously involved.

Melissa read her thoughts clearly and felt rage sweeping aside her shame. She couldn't altogether blame Ryan for what had happened, but never again would she allow herself to be so carried away. She could have reason to be grateful that Angela had arrived as she did.

'I was just going.' With a stiff smile for Angela she walked past her. As she had not brought a bag, there was nothing to retrieve and she was at the door before she remembered Ryan hadn't given her a definite decision about the holding.

Turning, she looked at him irresolutely. He was standing quite still, his hands stuck in his pockets, watching her. His expression was not encouraging, every hint of a smile having faded from his face, although he must have guessed what was worrying her.

Carefully, nerving herself to ignore Angela's increasing impatience, she searched for the right thing to say. 'Have you any message for Mum, Mr Trevelyan?'

His lips curled in an enigmatical smile again, awarding her diplomacy. 'I'll be down at your place about seven in the morning. I expect to see you around, then I'll have a word with your mother.'

It wasn't very reassuring, but she had to be content. She had half hoped he would offer to see her out and tell her, one way or another, on the way to the door. Obviously he intended she should suffer a sleepless night. Yet all she could think of, as she drove through the soft darkness, was Ryan alone with Angela Brett, in a house which only held the two of them.

Next morning she glanced at the heap of her discarded dress on the floor with distaste. Quite willing, in her half awake state, to believe in black magic, she felt the old material must hold supernatural properties. Last night seemed like a bad dream. She hoped this morning wouldn't prove a continuation.

Sluicing her face with ice cold water didn't make her feel much better. Dressing quickly in old jeans and a faded shirt, she ran hopefully downstairs, but the kitchen clock confirmed her suspicions that it was already after seven o'clock. Her longing for a cup of tea faded as fresh panic set in, and hearing Mary stirring through the floor above her she rushed out before she could be discovered. Ryan had been brief but explicit about seeing her first, but, on not finding her, he might have gone.

His car was parked by the greenhouses, out of sight of the house, and he was sitting idly on one of the benches in the potting shed. Melissa paused a moment, weak with relief that he was still there.

'Good morning, Miss Grant.' Did she imagine a slight wariness, as she hesitated in the doorway? Was he trying to work out whether she expected an apology, or a resumption of his amorous tendencies of the evening before? His 'Miss Grant' put her nicely in her place.

'Good morning.' She found it difficult to remove the tautness from her face but managed it with a forced smile. Her behaviour last night was like a bad dream she had no intention of repeating, while she had no doubt his approach came from a regrettable masculine urge to prove that her underlying fear of being kissed was rooted in sheer imagination.

'You'd better come in and close the door,' he commanded. And, as she frowned cautiously, 'You don't need to wonder if I'm preparing another assault. I don't think I could make the effort, this morning.'

She was relieved to hear it, although the coldness of

his manner wasn't so welcome and she braced herself to endure what she suspected was coming. Scarcely able to keep on looking at him, she turned her eyes to the floor, then flushed painfully as it brought back shameful memories.

Plunging immediately, she looked back at his oddly reflective face. She ignored every tightening inch of her body. 'Won't you tell me what decision you've come to?'

'After I have your assurance on one or two things.'

'Yes! I thought I'd told you ...'

'Not in the sane light of day.'

Was this another way of implying that last night had been anything but that, and he was making sure she shouldn't think otherwise?

Pride came to her aid, as she banged shut the door. 'I shouldn't have gone to Poldary last night if I'd known you were expecting Miss Brett.' There, that must prove clearly that she knew where his real intentions lay.

'I didn't say I was expecting anyone.'

'You must have done, if you told her Mrs Barr was away.' Melissa stiffened herself. 'Perhaps that's why you feel so tired this morning?'

His mouth tightened. 'I can't see what Angela has to do with my being here. I suggest we change the subject.'

It was an order, not a suggestion. 'I see.' Biting her lip, Melissa wavered. He was right, of course. The baleful expression fading from her eyes, she queried, 'This assurance you seek will be about my work?'

'Exactly, Miss Grant.'

Her dislike deepened. 'What exactly do you want me to promise?'

He stood up. As he stepped nearer the open neck of his shirt came level with her eyes and a sensation of molten warmth washed over her. She wanted to shrink back, but her muscles seemed to have lost the power to move.

His gaze went over her flatly as he towered above her, perhaps mistaking her trembling for rage. 'Just more or less what we'd already agreed, but you must accept one additional proviso.'

'Something else?' Why did she have such a sudden longing to touch the muscular arms, folded so indifferently over his chest? Then the desire melted in alarm as the full import of what he said really hit her. 'Surely,' she cried, 'there can't be anything more?'

'Yes,' he said crisply. 'I want you to promise that until we get this market garden back on its feet you will concentrate on it to the exclusion of everything else. With this in mind you must give up your present friendship with Barry Ward and Ben, when he returns from the States.'

Realising he had the whip hand didn't help. 'But you've no right to ask this of me!' she gasped, her inflammatory temper quickly flaring. 'Barry and Ben are personal, nothing to do with work, or the holding.'

'You know damned well these supposedly innocent friendships you've enjoyed have affected your work indirectly.' Ryan's eyes sparkled fire and mockery. 'You can't pretend boy-friends are essential, not feeling the way you do about men?'

'That doesn't say I can't be friends with them!' she protested sharply. 'What on earth am I to say to them?'

'Just tell them you're busy,' he reminded her grimly, adding pointedly, 'I hope you won't have to lie about that. If it's a friend you want, for the time being you'll just have to make do with me.'

'I don't think you've ever wanted to be my friend,' she spluttered.

'Quite right,' he muttered laconically, his hand going out to lift a strand of tumbled hair from off her brow, his fingers lingering on her temple, where the pulse hammered. 'I was thinking of your side of things. Don't pretend you find me too repulsive.'

Coming to her senses, she struck his hand away, not bothering to hide her revulsion. Speaking between her teeth, her eyes glowed with temper. 'I'd like to get a few things straight, before I allow myself to be overwhelmed by your generosity! I'm to work like a horse and give up all my friends?'

Darkly his eyes lifted from the red mark on his arm. 'Your masculine ones. I insist.'

'But your last proviso, that I bring all my worries to you, is optional?'

His nod was curt and cool, as if he regretted it. 'It was for your comfort, not mine.'

'So,' she pressed, a small devil driving her recklessly on, 'I can reject it without it making any difference to what you decide on?'

'You could regret it.'

'No.' Tossing back her shining head, she let disdain etch every fine-boned feature. 'Not if I live to be a thousand!'

'As you wish.' His switch to bored indifference was familiar, but this time, she realised, with mixed feelings, he meant it. 'Now, Miss Grant, let me get a few things straight, before I agree to seeing your mother. As well as giving up your boy-friends you must be at work by six each morning, and be willing to work until everyone is finished for the day. And you must consent to taking orders from me as well as other people.'

'What else can I do but agree?'

'You'd better. Last night you were ready to promise anything,' he reminded her, his eyes lingering on her lips, turning her hot and cold. 'I warn you, if you don't reform, Miss Grant, there will be no more chances. Next time I'll simply inform my solicitors and leave the country. I'm overdue for a visit to New Zealand anyway.'

Mary and Lewis were delighted when Ryan told them he was giving them another chance, only he didn't put it quite like that. He simply said there had been a mistake with his solicitor, that the letter they had received had been the result of a slight misunderstanding, which he had subsequently sorted out. He was so

glib over the breakfast table that Melissa wasn't really
surprised that Mary appeared to swallow the lot gratefully with her coffee, and Lewis looked too relieved to
probe even the weaker points of Ryan's story.

Mary, apparently throwing off the strain of the past
twenty-four hours, chatted to Ryan enthusiastically
about new plans, but after he had gone she sat down
and burst into tears. 'It's just a reaction,' she assured
her worried husband and daughter. 'I've been so worried, and now everything is all right again. What a
wonderful man Ryan is,' she added. 'I hope we all appreciate him.'

'Who could fail to?' Melissa muttered sullenly, while
Lewis awkwardly passed Mary a handkerchief and
begged her not to get upset.

Any hope of finding another way out of the situation
in which Melissa found herself faded as she watched
Mary drying her worn face. She was trapped between
her mother's tears and the man who had set himself
out so ruthlessly to run her life.

Lewis was as startled as she had ever seen him when
he arrived at the greenhouses next morning and found
her already there.

'Dear me!' he mocked, 'have you really turned over
a new leaf, or has our friend Ryan Trevelyan done it
for you?'

Melissa glanced at him warily, deciding to stick to
her former policy of half-truths. 'I don't like to see
Mum so worn, Lewis.' He would find she could hint
as well as he could!

He smiled, noting her sharpness. 'Be careful,' he
jibed. 'You don't want to turn into a proper little
shrew. I haven't had an opportunity to ask you how
you managed to change his lordship's mind.'

Melissa paled. 'His lordship?' She knew very well
to whom he referred, but she wanted time.

Grey eyebrows raised, Lewis advised, 'Quit stalling,
Melissa.'

Coldly she replied, 'All right! But you know I have

no influence with him. Nothing I might say could sway him, once he's made up his mind.'

'Hmm.' Lewis slanted her a long look, as she too busily inspected some newly sown seed. 'I wish I were better at reading people's faces. Mr Trevelyan's, when he stares at you, ought to tell me something.'

'Lewis!' Her face was hot; she hoped he put it down to all the work she had got through before he arrived. 'Ryan Trevelyan and I are barely on speaking terms. When he looks at me he's probably just trying to find something more to criticise.'

'I wonder?' Lewis shrugged. 'I still think you're going about him the wrong way.'

'Which is my business, not yours!' Melissa retorted fiercely, turning back to her seedboxes.

Two weeks later she was in the shop when Ryan walked in. It was the first time she had seen him since he had had breakfast with them and informed Mary of his decision. Since then things had gone on so normally she sometimes wondered if it had ever happened. It was only her own aching body which sometimes convinced her it had.

As her eyes met his she was conscious of his penetrating gaze, which noted the dark shadows under her eyes, her new thinness. 'Well, how are things going?' He held out his money for a newspaper. 'Keeping nice and busy?'

'As you told me to.' Quickly she passed his paper, averting her eyes from the hand that reached out to take it, averting her mind from the mockery she detected. The sleeves of his fawn cotton shirt were rolled up and the sinewy strength of his arms covered with fine dark hairs affected her oddly. A shot of electricity went through her as their fingers touched.

'I see you haven't lost your spirit,' he said dryly, 'but I don't expect you to wear yourself out.'

'At least my conscience is clear,' she retorted. 'I work hard each day, although I could have lain in bed for all you'd have known, as you haven't been near me.' So it could never seem she had missed him, she made her tone deliberately careless.

'If I'd heard of you being in bed I would have been here sooner.'

Her heartbeats quickened, then steadied. That obviously meant something else. 'You wouldn't have heard.'

Lazily his mouth quirked. 'You forget my spies.'

'Not really.' She felt better when gazing at him coldly. 'But I can't promise they'll always have nothing to report.'

His answering coldness was immediate. 'I seem to recall you've already promised me that, and it isn't something I'm prepared to review.'

CHAPTER EIGHT

MELISSA retreated into angry silence, wishing he hadn't come that morning and caught her in one of the smart new overalls Mary had brought her to wear in the shop. They were expensively stylish and, when Melissa wore them, didn't seem like overalls at all. Suddenly, looking at Ryan, she had a horrid suspicion where they had really come from.

Seeing her wearing one, he would assume she was conforming, and while fully aware that this was what she must do she hated the satisfaction it must be giving him.

'You've lost weight,' he said quietly, his glance moving purposefully from where the full curves of her figure pushed against the thin material, to her tightly belted, next-to-nothing waist.

She shrugged, colour tinting her high cheekbones as she tried not to feel as if he had actually touched her. 'I put in a long day and don't take one off.'

'It won't do you any real harm,' he said soberly, as she remembered unwillingly how she had felt in his arms. 'Are you complaining already?'

'No, I'm not!' she glared at him, wondering why the instant his eyes flicked her body her legs should feel like jelly.

'Are you asking for time off?' he enquired, again dryly, his eyes holding hers.

'No!' She glared at him resentfully; must he always expect the worst from her? Then she thought about Helen. Apprehension mingled with doubt as she bit her lip and turned from the plants she had rearranged three times, 'At least ...'

'Yes?' he prompted, an 'I knew it' twist to his lips.

Cautiously she dampened her sensitively curved

mouth. 'I had a telephone call today from my cousin Helen.'

'Ah, I see. Cousin Helen.' Why did he sound as if he was getting ready to pounce?

'She's been lonely since I left and would like to come and see me, to take me out for an hour.'

'I thought she no longer had anything to do with your mother and had disagreed irrevocably with you?'

'I know,' Melissa barely knew what else to say. 'I rather think she's regretted letting me go. I suppose it's because I was with her a long time. Naturally we were very fond of each other.'

His face had gone expressionless, but instinctively Melissa felt he was angry, although he didn't show it. 'That's all behind you now.' His hands came down heavily on her shoulders, as if to emphasise his words.

Resentment tightened the deep unhappiness inside her. 'You can't just throw off affection like an old coat!'

'Perhaps not.' His eyes glinted. 'All the same, you'd better tell her not to come here.'

Not to come here! Ryan's short, terse sentence echoed through her head as she sagged away from him against the wall. It was as if the race of their tense conversation had exhausted her, leaving her curiously shaken. She could see the lines of his mouth held hard, almost as if he was willing her to accept his orders. She might be mistaken, but his mouth was as far as she dared go; she couldn't meet his eyes.

'But I can't!' She found her voice at last. 'I can't just say I won't see her. She only wants to talk to me.'

Ryan closed up on her then, his fingers under her chin, forcing her to look at him as she tried to ignore the warmth spread by the contact. 'Cousin Helen will come here, dangling her wealth like a carrot.'

'And you think I'm a rabbit?'

'Hardly that,' he gave a slight smile, 'but you've wallowed in the lap of luxury for a long time. I don't know what influence she still has over you.'

'You aren't exactly a poor man yourself!' Melissa retaliated.

'My assets lie mostly in land,' he said grimly. 'I live comfortably, but I don't think there's much in my house to suggest over-indulgence. I try to use my spare cash constructively, not on spoiling little girls.'

'Just ones like Angela, perhaps?' He gave her an opening she couldn't resist.

'She could be worth spoiling occasionally,' he agreed.

Her drawn breath did nothing to soothe the hurt she had asked for. 'I'd like to tell you how much I dislike you, Ryan Trevelyan,' she spluttered, 'but I know when my hands are tied. One point I can make clear—I'm not a little girl!'

'Something you've only discovered since you left Cousin Helen,' he drawled, 'but I found it out the first time I kissed you—or was it the second?' His head went back to study her consideringly. 'I can't remember exactly when you realised yourself. I only recall an appreciable difference.'

This was something she didn't want even to think about. Melissa concentrated on Cousin Helen, rather than admit Ryan was very near the truth. 'Helen might help Mum,' she said, her colour heightening betrayingly.

'Then you wouldn't need me. Is that what you mean?' His hands tightened. 'You might be wiser to think again. Do you want to risk finding out, if she did try to buy you back, if your mother would be willing to accept a few paltry pounds in return for her daughter? If she did accept, you'd have to be prepared to weigh the hurt you'd receive against possible benefits. Of course there's always Freddy.'

'How do you know about him?' The advice he had given faded before a new apprehension. Had she told him?

'I know more than you think. You forget I know a lot of people. My world doesn't begin and end at Poldary.'

Defensively, to hide the cold she suddenly felt,

Melissa cried, 'Freddy has nothing to do with this—this visit of Helen's. No matter what I say she might come. She never used to take much notice of me.'

'This time you'd better see she does!' His voice was crisp with warning as his hand again left her shoulder to curve the taut line of her jaw. Before she could move he bent his head and crushed his mouth against hers.

She would have cried out with pain if she had been able to. Eyes closed, she fought him, her mouth tightly shut against the insistence of his, her hands clutching wildly. The control he had over her was devastating, his sensuous kisses far more frightening than Freddy's mild ones had ever been. When her lips could no longer retain their former tenseness his mouth triumphed as he thrust them apart, and no sound escaped her as molten nectar seemed to pour down her throat.

As her old fear soared, then left her, she realised she was fighting no one but herself. With a little moan she allowed herself to be crushed against his hard, muscled chest as he reacted to her small, feverish sigh by pulling her closer into his arms. His searing passion broke over her as the pressure of his mouth became implacably demanding, sweeping her along on a wave of feeling that made mockery of all her previous terrors.

When at last he lifted his head, coherent thought was so drowned it was seconds before she could look at him. When she did the expression in his eyes frightened her.

'You're learning.' His breathing was heavy on her face and his thumb still lay on the pulse which raced in her throat, where his hand slid as he drew away from her. 'Doesn't this tempt you not to return to Cousin Helen?'

Melissa's heart slumped. She hadn't wanted him to kiss her, but he had only done so for his own ends. To keep her here, to work in the market garden. With an effort she stepped back from his persuasively caressing hand, stiffening in sudden outrage as the movement she made brought his hand down over the rounded outline of her breast. 'Now who's dangling the carrot?' she flared.

A moment later he was away from her as another customer came through the door. 'I don't want another man taking over before I'm ready,' he said, with an arrogant intimacy that made her tremble. 'Just tell Helen you're too busy,' he advised, smiling briefly at the woman who had entered, before leaving by the same door.

After the woman had gone Melissa sank down on the chair her mother had placed by the counter for the convenience of customers. It had been a real effort to serve the woman, to endure her curious glances, which obviously sprang from Ryan's abrupt departure and Melissa's rumpled hair. Her strength appeared to have left her, as it did each time he held her in his arms. The weight of his lean yet heavy body was punishing, but it was her own response to the hard demands of his mouth she remembered most. She had little doubt he knew exactly what he was doing, and the knowledge awoke the anger which so quickly turned into something else when he held her to him. In his arms the world she knew whirled into chaos with wild, exotic fire striking right through her. He inflamed her senses, incited and quickened exhilarating emotions, whetted appetites she had never known existed and managed to terrify her at the same time.

Momentarily she panicked. Did he imagine he could do with her exactly as he liked? Order her around, treat her like a half-wit, rule her very life as well as her emotions? And were these same emotions, the physical ones she had thought she hated, ironically going to prove her greatest weakness? No, never, she vowed, jumping quickly to her feet again. To fall in love with Ryan Trevelyan, to get involved with him in any way, would be sheer madness! He would simply trample the new-born emotions she feared into the ground, should she be foolish enough to give in to him.

Clearly at odds with such satisfactorily harder feelings, a tear ran down her cheek and she had just rubbed it impatiently away when Angela Brett walked in. Her head still reeling, Melissa looked at her numbly. It just wasn't her day, but she might as well have the lot. She had thought the worst was over, but if the expression on Angela's face was anything to go by, it was yet to come. Perhaps the other girl had seen Ryan leaving and had come to discover the exact purpose of his visit. She mightn't believe he had only come to buy a newspaper.

'Can I help you?' she asked at last, when Angela made no effort to speak.

'Not really.' Angela's lips twisted, in what Melissa took to be a smile. 'I'm just looking.'

'Oh, feel free,' Melissa replied with exaggerated courtesy, which she didn't feel at all guilty about Angela noticing.

With apparent indifference Angela picked up a small cactus, glancing at it briefly before putting it down again. 'How do you like working in a shop?' she asked, with an acid sweetness.

'No better or worse than thousands of other people do, I suppose,' Melissa retorted carefully.

Angela permitted herself a careless yawn. 'Poor things! I've often pitied them, slaving away from nine till five.'

Melissa doubted if Angela had ever really pitied anyone in her whole life. 'Someone has to do it,' she said stiffly.

'Oh, yes!' Angela's brows rose expressively. 'I quite agree. I expect, for those with parents too poor to support them, it's a blessing to have any job at all. I've never had to work, of course. Daddy's always had plenty of money.'

Drawing a deep breath, Melissa stared at her. Funnily enough she remembered, with shame, how she had once felt rather superior herself to the crowds of girls who had to rush out to shops and offices each morning. But that was when she had lived with Cousin

Helen. Having to work here, in the shop and house, wherever she was most needed, had, to begin with anyway, dented her pride considerably. It was only lately she had realised she was getting back her proper sense of values. The holding might be small and unpretentious, but the raising of good crops for sale must be more worthwhile than being a snob. If it still hurt a little to have someone like Angela throwing sharp little taunts, it was something her pride would soon get over.

The confusion such thoughts brought to her rueful face must have convinced Angela she had been well and truly humiliated, as she smiled condescendingly before continuing, 'Didn't I see Mr Trevelyan leaving?'

'He called for his newspaper,' Melissa was annoyed with herself for explaining. 'Didn't he see you? I mean, if you saw him.'

'No,' Angela didn't seem too upset, 'I don't believe he did, and I was down by the greenhouses, too far away to attract his attention. Your stepfather was showing me some of his bonsai trees. Quite fascinating.'

'You can always call at Poldary on your way home,' Melissa said dryly, suspecting this was something Angela always did, whenever she had the opportunity. Busily she began weighing young rhubarb into pound bundles, hoping Angela would take the hint and go.

Angela didn't. Shooting a quick glance at Melissa, she idly picked up a piece of rhubarb. 'Whoever buys this around here? Daddy's gardener gives huge quantities away each year.'

Patiently Melissa waited.

Dropping the piece of rhubarb suddenly, Angela exclaimed, 'I suppose I'd better hurry if I'm to catch Ryan for coffee. While Mrs Barr was away I was at Poldary almost every day, helping with his meals. When he wasn't able to dine with us, of course. Mrs Barr is back, but he still likes seeing me around.'

'It must have been a great comfort for him to have you,' Melissa said tartly.

'Oh, yes!' Angela's smile was exaggerated and

dreamy. 'Naturally he appreciates everything I do, although he declares he won't allow his wife to work when he marries.'

Completely shocked, Melissa didn't take time to think that one out. 'You're going to be married?'

'We might. It appears to surprise you?'

Melissa couldn't truthfully say it did, so just shook her head speechlessly and tried to ask herself what did it matter who Ryan married.

Angela's eyes narrowed. 'I'm glad you don't really doubt it.'

'Why should I?' Melissa wondered desperately where her mother was. 'I don't know either of you very well but I'd have thought you'd be ideally suited.' Even Angela should be satisfied with that—if she didn't think about it too deeply!

'No, you don't do you?' Angela sounded regretful but didn't look it. 'Actually this was something I mentioned to Ryan only the other day, but he explained how he didn't want to encourage you, although he did admit you amused him.'

'Amused him?' Sharply, her face paling, Melissa swung around. 'What did he mean by that?'

'I didn't mean to upset you,' Angela purred, 'but he isn't used to girls like you invading his privacy. That evening I found you together in the kitchen at Poldary he told me you'd practically barged in and begged him to kiss you.'

Melissa, struck silent for a long moment, was relieved she had restrained herself when Mary came in. Bitterness and an over-hasty tongue might have proved an unwise combination, especially with Angela probably ready to repeat to Ryan everything she said. What mutual pleasure it must give them to be able to discuss the faults of someone like herself; but how could Ryan have laughed after holding her in his arms? And he must have told Angela, for how otherwise could she have known? Bitterly Melissa wondered why he hadn't confessed that it had been his lips which had taken hers so ruthlessly. She might have provoked him, but never intentionally as far as that. But it had been his mouth which had been so strongly persuasive, his body that hadn't been able to hide his eagerness to possess hers. Almost he had made her forget her fundamental terror of such things, but never again! Men were opportunists, ready to play off one girl against another. This time, Melissa decided angrily, she had learnt a lesson, one she wouldn't forget!

'What did she want?' Mary asked, as Angela, with a brief word, departed, a more than satisfied smile on her face. 'She looked like someone who'd made a good buy, but I didn't notice her carrying anything.'

Melissa shrugged, trying to look indifferent. 'She was just pondering over Lewis's bonsai.' She picked up one of the miniature trees and touched a branch gently with her long, slender fingers. 'I think she changed her mind, though, as she didn't buy one.'

'I noticed Ryan was here.'

'Yes,' Melissa answered stiffly, wondering who else was going to comment on it, 'he was.'

Anxiously Mary frowned. 'You two haven't had words again?'

'No, not really,' Melissa jerked out, as Mary stared doubtfully. 'He was just being generous with his advice.'

'Which you didn't care for?'

'Well, he does like rubbing me up the wrong way and, all things considered, I think he has a nerve!' Melissa's voice hardened. 'I didn't say much, but if he'd come in after Miss Brett, not before, I might have said more!'

'Oh, Melissa! You promised you wouldn't upset him,' Mary exclaimed.

'No, Mum, I won't. Not if I can help it,' she agreed. 'But you realise I'm promising this for your sake, not his!'

'I didn't think you cared about me,' Mary said painfully.

'Of course I do.' Melissa didn't say she was surprised to find she really did at last. Affection for her mother, which she thought had died, was growing stronger each day. Not that she could forget what had caused it to diminish in the first place, but it didn't seem to come between them any more. If all there remained of the shock she had received as a child were a few personal abhorrences, this was her problem, not Mary's. And she might still find some way of avenging herself on Ryan and Angela Brett without involving her mother.

The next afternoon when the telephone rang Melissa answered it. It was Mrs Barr from Poldary. Mr Trevelyan was giving a dinner party and she wanted to order vegetables and flowers. 'He said you would bring them, Melissa.'

The way in which Mrs Barr uttered her name made Melissa want to refuse. She obviously wasn't in the same class as Angela any more, but judging from Mrs Barr's tone she might have been the lowest of the low. 'I'll be there,' Melissa assured her grimly, 'when I feel like it!'

Such odd bits of defiance were about all that kept her going, she thought ruefully, as she drove to Poldary later, the back seat of the car full with Mrs Barr's order. The scent of flowers was almost overpowering, and she wondered what sort of party Ryan was having. Surely it must be something rather special to warrant the show all these blooms would make. Mary had sent their best. Suddenly Melissa felt quite sick. It couldn't be an engagement party? Ryan and Angela's? The car swerved across the road and had to be righted. What if it was? she shrugged tensely. It wouldn't be altogether unexpected.

Yet the thought of Angela and Ryan in each other's arms was more than she could take calmly, and so busy was she trying unhappily to find other reasons for his party that she found herself at the front of Poldary before she realised. Startled, she became aware that Angela's smart little car was parked outside the door and she was standing there, talking to Ryan.

Melissa jammed on her brakes, causing the gravel to fly, and Angela to literally jump out of the way. Melissa saw how she glanced at her before clutching Ryan's arm, her face the picture of injured distress, and her lips curled cynically as she watched.

Her contemptuous expression must have shown as there was something deadly about Ryan as he stood there, staring at her. He didn't speak, he waited until she swung her slight, jean-clad figure half out of the door.

'I have your order,' she informed him coolly. 'You could help me carry it into the house.'

'Indeed, Miss Grant, I will not!' His voice resembled soft steel. It was in his eyes, too. 'The tradesmen's entrance is clearly signposted on the back drive. You will go there at once, after apologising to Miss Brett, and carry everything out yourself, not forgetting to put it all exactly where Mrs Barr wants it.'

'No, I won't!' she cried, on her feet in a flash, her humble new resolutions forgotten. How dared he speak to her like this in front of Angela Brett?

He dared more. As if he forgot Angela was an interested spectator, his hands shot out brutally to grasp Melissa's thinly clad shoulders and shake her. 'Another word out of you,' he gritted furiously, 'and you can go. The whole damned lot of you!'

Melissa, managing to free herself, went colourless, and for a moment Ryan looked as if he felt he had gone too far. 'Melissa,' he said shortly, 'Look here . . .'

'I'm sorry,' she interrupted starkly, 'I didn't think.'

There was a whiteness under his skin as his eyes flicked swiftly from her shocked face to Angela, obviously wishing the latter was not there. 'If only——'

'I know,' Melissa's voice was brittle with her efforts to stop crying, as she cut in again, 'if only I would learn my place!' Numbly she groped her way back into the car. 'Don't worry, I will.'

Jerking away, before he could say more, she fancied

his expression was mixed, but she couldn't clearly read it. Angela's was another matter. Her triumph was so plain to be seen it took no more than a fleeting glance to assess it.

As usual, Melissa's apprehension and remorse didn't last long. Her temper mounting at the way Ryan had spoken to her, his threat to her and her family, she stirred more gravel on her way to the back door. Once there she sat for a few minutes trying to control her trembling hands for fear Mrs Barr might notice how distraught she was. Then, after lifting everything out, she went to find Mrs Barr so she might know exactly where to put it. She opened the back door quietly, intending to knock on the kitchen one as Mrs Barr never appeared to hear otherwise.

Approaching the kitchen, down the long passage, she heard voices. As she hesitated, unseen, she heard Angela exclaim, 'You should have seen her, Mrs Barr, driving to the front as though she owned the place!'

'Really, Miss Angela?'

'Yes, Mrs Barr, you've every right to look scandalised, but you should have seen how Ryan dealt with her. Of course he realises what a jumped-up little trollop she is. He said she's getting to be a proper nuisance. Now, about this dinner ...'

Quietly Melissa tiptoed back the way she had come. Carefully she stacked the vegetables and flowers just inside the door and left. Her anger was spreading, invading every vein in her body. Had Ryan really said that? Quite probably he did consider her of no account and had no qualms about expressing such an opinion. And to think she had imagined he had regretted his abruptness, after he had shaken her!

Melissa drew a deep breath which sounded suspiciously like a sob as she pressed her foot recklessly to the floorboards. Both he and Angela were despicable. Neither intended that she should keep an ounce of pride. Until half an hour ago she hadn't thought she had much left, but now she felt it surging blindly again. So they'd decided she was a little nobody? Well, she would show them!

Concentrating on how best to bring this about, she was home before she had found the answer. There was something, but it was so improbable she doubted if it would work. Perspiration breaking out on her forehead even to think of such a daring plan, she drove on past the house until she came to a stretch of wooded hillside, bordering the moors. Turning the car on to the edge of a rutted track, she parked where she had a clear view of the distant sea. The road was deserted and, on the lane, her tires crunched on last year's dried twigs and grass, hidden under a growth of new greenery. From where she sat she could see the long rollers of the Channel and the white flash of smaller waves breaking softly on the sandy shores. Getting out of the car, she walked a little way through the woods, where in spring, as a child, she had gathered bluebells. Now the bluebells had finished flowering, their green leaves all covered with bracken, dark green and waist-high. Struggling through them she came to a clearing where, forgetting she ought to be working, she sat down and began to meditate.

An hour later, on returning to the holding, she found Mary looking harassed.

'Thank heaven you're back!' she exclaimed when she saw Melissa. 'The telephone has never stopped ringing!'

'Not for me, surely?' Because none of her new ideas had survived the lengthy consideration she had given them, she felt depressed, too much so to be interested in what Mary was saying.

'Two were. At least two concerned you.' Mary paused, brushing a soapy hand over her forehead. 'Ryan rang.'

'Ryan?'

'Yes. He wanted to speak to you, but when I told him you were still out he said it didn't matter, that he would call this evening.'

'But what about his dinner party?'

'I don't know. He might only be calling for a few minutes. I'm just telling you what he said.' She didn't notice Melissa's uneasy face. 'Then there was Helen.'

'Helen?' Melissa started guiltily. After Ryan's lecture she had put off getting in touch with her and Helen must have tried again.

Mary sighed fretfully. 'Yes, I thought you'd be surprised. Actually she asked if she could call to see me and bring some of your clothes. I suppose she might as well, as they won't fit anyone else. She's off on a long cruise in the near future, so I expect she really wants to ask you to go with her.'

'What did you say to her?'

Pausing again, Mary looked steadily at Melissa's taut face. 'In view of what you said this afternoon,' she smiled, 'I told her she was welcome.'

'Thanks, Mum.' Melissa hugged her mother gratefully, 'I still mean it—so I won't be cruising. She ought to take you.' As Mary sighed wryly and went on with her dishes, Melissa asked quickly, 'Didn't Ryan ask why I wasn't here?'

'No, why should he? He would know you were on your way back from delivering the produce Mrs Barr ordered.' Mary glanced over her shoulder more anxiously. 'You will be here to see him tonight?'

'Yes,' Melissa nodded abstractedly, but Mary was apparently satisfied as she said nothing more. After another minute she dried her hands and went out, leaving Melissa to stare rather blindly after her.

For the past hour she had sat in the woods, an exercise which had proved a sheer waste of time when she had reached the unhappy conclusion that the idea she had to avenge herself of Angela, and subsequently Ryan, was both impractical and ridiculous, to say nothing of being dangerous! Hot with mortification, she had been aghast that such a silly scheme had ever entered her head. Hurt pride couldn't justify allowing even her thoughts to go to such lengths. Now she was glad she had come to her senses in time, although she wasn't quite sure how much more she could put up with from Angela.

Finishing at six, she had a warm shower, washing her hair while she was busy, closing her eyes as the rinsing water ran down her face and over the gleaming softness of her breasts. Remembering how taut they had gone under Ryan's hands, she flinched with embarrassment, reaching quickly for a towel. Why did she have to recall such things? It could only be that she disliked having him near her.

Combing her hair, she set it in soft, shining waves before lightly making up her face. Putting on a thin, checked shirt, she ran downstairs. 'If Ryan calls,' she said to Mary, who was sitting discussing the next day's work with Lewis, 'I'll be somewhere in the gardens. If it's really me he wants to see!'

She was there when he came and, for all her cool determination to forget it, she was unable to look at him after the way he had spoken to her earlier. What did he want now? Half convinced Mary must have been mistaken, she felt a curious sickness in her throat as she watched his tall figure striding towards her.

Suddenly she knew why he was here. She stared at him, wide-eyed, as he halted beside her. 'I know what it is. You've come to remind me I didn't apologise to Angela.'

'No, you didn't, did you?' His mouth twisted as he looked down on her and for all her resolve she let her temper rise.

He had come for the sole purpose of reminding her, not to bury the hatchet. What a fool she had been to imagine he might be suffering remorse. Suddenly the plans she had made, then so abruptly dismissed, didn't seem so ridiculous after all. Be nice to Ryan for a change, her thoughts had whispered. Smile at him, entice him a little. He's only a man and might be intrigued if nothing else. Flutter your lashes, they're long enough. Lower your neckline, lead him on discreetly and see how Angela likes it!

All this, which she had rejected as wild, in more ways than one, came flooding back, sweeping her irrevocably along. Recklessly she found herself whispering meekly, the pride in her heart overriding common sense, 'I'm sorry, Ryan. I meant to apologise, but I'm afraid it just slipped my mind. I realise I have a temper, but you must make allowances for my hair.' Almost unable to believe she could act so well, she felt a guilty colour wash her cheeks. She would never have believed her own capacity for deceit. Quickly she closed her eyes as remorse began to hit her.

Ryan smiled slowly and not without a flicker of relief. 'It certainly makes a nice change to hear you say you're sorry,' he said dryly. Placing a hand on her arm, he tilted her chin with the other, so she had to look at him again. 'Now, it's my turn. I shouldn't have spoken as I did, but you have a rare knack of making me say things—and act—in a way I'm sorry for afterwards. Melissa . . .' he hesitated.

'What about your dinner party?' she whispered, hurriedly, not sure she could take over much of his new gentleness. Yet the slight smile she forced to her lips unconsciously hinted at a lingering hurt. 'I don't want to keep you.'

'It's not until tomorrow,' he replied indifferently. 'It's not important.'

So it couldn't be an engagement celebration! Relief made her feel almost lightheaded with a strange joy. 'Oh, I see.'

Ryan's hand went gently to her hair. 'It's too beautiful,' he teased softly, 'to be blamed for everything you say.'

There was a small silence as she glanced up at him and it shocked her to see the way his eyes lingered over her. But it was a shock that excited and disturbed and aroused a response more potent than she knew how to deal with. He smiled in a way that started her heart over-reacting again and the smile she gave him in return was shy but wholly spontaneous. Everything else faded from her mind.

'You've worked hard,' his hand moved on her hair, as if unable to resist the silky feel of it. 'How would you like a chance to relax? Have dinner with me?'

Would it be relaxing? Wonderingly her eyes darkened a little. 'At Poldary?'

'No, not at Poldary.' He seemed to understand her reluctance without an explanation. 'I know a place along the coast, where we can eat well in very pleasant surroundings, and where there're never very many people. On the other hand, if you prefer somewhere more lively there's a much wider choice.'

Looking into his unreadable eyes she found it impossible to refuse. The market garden, its evening silence broken only by birdsong, faded away, leaving only the two of them. At that moment there seemed so much accord between them she had to fight to keep Angela's image before her. It was difficult to believe she and Ryan had ever experienced such differences of opinion, had ever snapped and snarled at each other, hurt and hounded each other until, raw and wounded, she had been forced to retreat from each fresh scene. She didn't even know if she was retreating now. Capitulation, surrender, were words she thrust nervously from her. Fooling the enemy, was the phrase she must stick to—if she was able.

Taking a deep breath, she looked away. 'I'm not—dressed.'

'We don't have to be formal.' He was talking very slowly and quietly, as if not willing to risk a harsh note spoiling the surprising new tranquillity between them. 'I think I'll do, but you could always go and slip into a dress.'

Now she had to look at him again. He wore a pale blue shirt and his trousers, tightly belted, were immaculately cut, and cunningly fashioned to the powerful length of his hips and legs.

'Melissa,' he forced her to meet his eyes as his voice

lingered over her name, 'what do you think?'

'I'd—I'd like to.' She had been going to say, quite spontaneously, she'd love to, but the sick feeling returned. Deceiving Ryan was going to mean doubting every sincere word which sprang to her lips. It would mean the mixing of her every genuine and dishonest feeling, to the extent where she mightn't know which was which. Deceiving him might eventually lead her into such a tangle she wouldn't be able to find her way out.

She nodded but could not speak, not even when he put an arm around her and drew her gently closer. 'Has it been so bad?'

There was compassion in his voice and his arms were tender, and again she forgot about Angela. Her need for comfort had never seemed greater. Tears unexpectedly stung her eyes. She found herself clinging, her voice muffled against his chest. 'Sometimes . . .'

His laughter was low, faintly triumphant. 'We'll have to see if we can't improve some things, change them perhaps, after we get to know each other better.' As she nodded, he lifted her chin again and his eyes seemed to soften and seduce. 'You've erected your own little barriers and I've been too rough. But I have been waiting for a sign.'

His lips were only a breath away when she drew back, the old fear gripping her by the throat, thrusting aside the excitement, the expectancy which flashed through her as he spoke, so that she flinched.

This time, however, her involuntary reaction didn't appear to arouse his impatience. Quietly he turned her around, letting her go but capturing her hand to walk her back to the house.

CHAPTER NINE

LEAVING Ryan in the kitchen talking to Mary and Lewis, Melissa ran upstairs and changed quickly from her jeans into a long skirt and matching top, one of the two evening outfits she had brought from Helen's place. The one she had worn at Ryan's party was probably too formal for a casual outing and, while he might have forgotten it, she felt like a change.

After dressing she made up her face carefully, but more to give her quivering nerves a chance to steady than from any desire to impress Ryan unduly. She still felt too stunned by what was happening to be able to see anything clearly. Such understanding, she supposed, would come later, in the form of satisfaction, or fear. She had a sinking feeling the latter would predominate. What she was doing might be reprehensible but surely not criminal, and neither Ryan nor Angela were exactly the most helpless of opponents. So, she assured herself, she didn't need to feel that way.

The hotel Ryan chose was along the coast, well set back off the road and very cosy with its oak-beamed ceilings and candlelit tables. The candles on their table glowed like pale primroses against the dark panelling, their flames bowing and fluttering with every small whisper of draught. By contrast, across the table, Ryan's eyes were cool, holding Melissa's sardonically, as if like herself he didn't altogether trust the new, friendly atmosphere between them.

'We can always drink to it,' he suggested dryly.

She hadn't the courage to pretend not to understand what he meant, but was glad he spoke softly. His voice was like a caress for all his irony. It played on her ears, beguiling her senses, so that she felt his mouth there. Her fingers, near trembling, she lifted the glass she had carried from the bar when the waiter told them their table was ready. 'Of course,' she agreed tentatively.

He continued to speak gently. 'There's no harm in trying.'

'No.' She didn't have the power to remove her gaze from his as the feeling of being absolutely at one with him continued. He stared into her eyes, his nostrils tensing. She felt he was trying to read her every small thought, but so imprisoned did she feel by his steady appraisal she was unable to look away.

He looked her over, the soft top which clung to her figure doing nothing to disguise the shapeliness within. His very masculine surveillance was thorough, skimming over her and not lacking in appreciation. He lifted his hand, leaning nearer to bring it down on hers, where it lay clenched on the table.

'You're looking very lovely tonight, Melissa.'

'I feel it, with you sitting by me.' She searched through her past experiences for the kind of smart repartee she had been so used to hearing and didn't remove her hand from under his. If he felt her pulse beating too rapidly it could only please him, as he would believe it was because of him.

She tried to smile and the way he smiled back brought the colour to her cheeks, making her unfortunately aware that she was too far behind the flirtatious expertise of her former friends to make the catching up easy. But then a man like Ryan Trevelyan would never be easy! Her own frightened, uneven heartbeats warned her this was no simple, friendly experience she was embarking on, but a frightening journey laced with pitfalls. Sitting so close to him, on the bench seat against the wall, she was suddenly fully conscious that she might never survive the first hour.

They had ordered in the bar and she knew relief when their waiter arrived with the first course—courgettes stuffed with local crab and tomatoes, and coated with cheese sauce. As the waiter served them, Ryan didn't immediately remove his hand, although he must have felt the hot little tug of her fingers.

'Doesn't the fresh air give you an appetite?' he asked, as Melissa made no attempt to eat the luscious portion on her plate.

'Oh, yes, of course!' She had been staring blindly at her courgette. Picking up a fork, she glanced up at him quickly, becoming entangled again in dark, probing eyes. 'I was just thinking.'

'What about?' When she didn't answer, his hand once more covered hers. I wouldn't think too much at the moment, if I were you. I believe you've done too much of it in the past. If you have to think everything out before you speak, plan every movement, you'll never get much pleasure out of life because enjoyment is usually spontaneous. Too much thought can kill it dead. This afternoon, in the garden, I took you by surprise. I didn't give you time to ponder as to how you should act. And what happens? You found yourself actually smiling at me, Ryan, the enemy, agreeing to go out with me. It wasn't until you reached your room that you paused to wonder if you'd done the right thing.'

'Oh,' she gasped, staring at him, her mouth half open in a whirlpool of confusion, 'how did you guess!'

He shook his head imperceptibly, then leant sideways, kissing her lips lightly. 'I had an odd fancy to do that in the garden. That I've succeeded now where I didn't before might tell a tale.'

He was too devious! Nervously she wondered how much he really guessed. Needing it, she reached for her wine, taking a quick gulp. When she put it down he picked it up, drinking deeply from where her lips had been. As she watched, her heart racing, he turned and kissed her mouth again, his still damp.

One moment his breath, his mouth was on hers, the next away, the whole thing completed so swiftly she doubted if anyone in the large, dimly lit room had noticed. Not that anyone was likely to object if they had as most of the other diners were in the same age group as Ryan and herself, but even such a brief salute caused the blood to race through Melissa's body.

Turning from her contemplatively, he began his meal but she felt too dazed to move a finger. Always she had hated being kissed and, earlier in her bedroom, she had been vaguely worried that this new exercise might involve too much of it. Ryan Trevelyan wouldn't go in for purely platonic friendships. Yet here she was wanting him to kiss her again, her old terror rapidly disappearing. She had wanted that kiss to deepen, wanted to feel his hard body pressing against hers. The couch on which they sat could have been a bed for her strangely wanton desires, the people around them the trees of the forest for all they might have bothered her if Ryan had chosen that moment to make passionate love to her.

'What's wrong now?' Smiling, he picked up her fork, placing it between her numb fingers himself, his mood teasing, indulgent. 'Come on, eat up. You must need all your strength.'

Shyly she forced her fingers to close around the fork, rather than return the pressure of his, but she scarcely realised what she was eating. Now she thought she knew what he meant when he advised her to let her senses take over. While eating, he couldn't easily hold her hand, but she could feel the hardness of his leg occasionally touching hers, as if he considered such contact necessary. When he turned to speak to her, twice he ran his arm along the back of the seat and placed his hand on her shoulder, as if the silky smoothness of her skin pleased him. And once his mouth followed the direction of his hand.

'You have the most delightful profile I've ever seen,' he murmured, as they waited for coffee. She was staring away from him across the room, as if seeking unconsciously with her eyes to escape what he was doing to her body. His voice was deep, velvety, she had discovered, when his emotions were aroused.

'Thank you.' She tried to speak coolly, while every

part of her responded hotly.

His expression, as his eyes rested on her face, was brooding but not harsh. Unexpectedly eager, she turned to him again, breathlessly waiting for him to go on.

His smile twisted, but he didn't disappoint her. 'Such a charming little nose, such classic lines to your chin and throat.' His smile broadened derisively, as her eyes widened, as if she'd never received such compliments in her life. 'You're very beautiful, Melissa, but I don't imagine I'm the first man to tell you so.'

'No ...' Again losing herself in his eyes, she was barely aware of what she was saying..

His smile tightened. 'Three men I know of.'

'Three? Oh, I see what you mean.' Her words were running into each other as though she had taken too much wine. 'Ben, Barry and Freddy. But they aren't important.'

'You must make sure they are not!' Again the harder mould to his mouth, a certain sensuous infliction of his will over hers. 'You must begin learning to concentrate on me.'

She tried to sound amused, anything to break the rather frightening tension springing up between them. 'As the others aren't around, I can't really do anything else.'

'Does that mean you would if you could?' the grip on her hand narrowed cruelly, curbing any frivolity.

'Not really ...' She winced.

'Do you want to go back to the bar?' he asked abruptly, steering her out of the dining room. 'Or home?'

Something had displeased him and her breathing constricted. Was it the hesitancy in the answer she had given him about the other men? Wasn't it silly to endanger the new harmony between them by allowing him to believe she was seriously interested in any of them? In the past it had taken little to set them at each other's throats. She mustn't risk this happening again!

Yet before she could speak someone cried, over Ryan's shoulder, 'Darling! Fancy seeing you here!'

Melissa, though stung by shock, sighed. She might have known they could never escape Angela! As the girl seized Ryan's arm, hugging it joyfully, Melissa wondered if some built-in radar told Angela where to find him. She remembered the first time Ryan had taken her out how Angela had turned up. Melissa frowned. It was all part of her scheme that Angela should find out about her new friendship with Ryan, but she would have welcomed a few more days.

As Angela caught sight of her, the crowd she was with attracted Melissa almost as much. Barry Ward was there with his sister and another couple. She hadn't known Barry knew Angela.

Angela stiffened abruptly when she discovered Melissa was with Ryan. 'Oh!' she exclaimed, her tone betraying she didn't believe it. 'Are you together?'

'A sort of working dinner,' Ryan drawled, obviously confusing Angela as he pulled Melissa back to his side. 'I was just about to take her home.'

A working dinner! So he felt it necessary to make an excuse? Melissa bit her lip hard, ignoring the pain. Was he indicating subtly that they still had a lot of ground to make up?

Whatever he meant, Angela looked suddenly relieved. Her face all smiles, she gazed up at him and cried, 'You can't go home yet, Ryan! We were just going into the bar. Why don't you join us?'

Melissa was sure she wasn't included in the invitation, but before Ryan could reply an imp of mischief caused her to nod quickly. 'I'd love to stay a little longer, darling. I haven't seen Barry or Susan for ages.'

While Barry and Susan welcomed her happily, she heard Angela saying icily that it was really remarkable who people knew these days. She sounded so vindictive Melissa felt her sudden bravado fade a little and she hoped her decision to stay had been a wise one. As well as her wishing to annoy Angela it had risen from a rather urgent desire to show Ryan she wasn't on any-thing but friendly terms with Barry, but, from the suspicious way he was watching Barry, it didn't seem he was going to be easily convinced.

As they moved to the bar she noticed how Susan and the other girl both appeared attracted by Ryan's dark good looks and a shiver of something she couldn't de-fine went through her. The other girl, Samantha, who Melissa gathered was a model, wore a long, sophisti-cated skirt with slits down the side with a top which scarcely existed. She sat on the other man's knee and the amount of flesh she exposed made Melissa blush, although it didn't apparently disturb the others. Ryan only seemed amused, even when he must have noticed Melissa's hand, which still mysteriously remained in his, tighten with embarrassment.

Someone put money into a machine and several couples danced to the catchy tune which poured forth. Barry asked Melissa and she circled the room with him while Angela passed triumphantly in Ryan's arms. Ryan didn't appear to object to the way Angela clung, and again Melissa felt that indefinable shiver.

When the music stopped it was Barry, this time, who fed the machine, but before he could ask Melissa to dance again, Ryan claimed her. It was a dreamy, sensuous waltz, chosen by Barry with Melissa in mind. Now he was forced to watch as Ryan carried her away.

Ryan held her close, his hand on her back firmly pinning her against him. 'You could have danced with Angela,' she muttered defiantly, apprehensive of the way he could make her feel. How could she work to any plan with the blood pounding in her ears and a devastating sweetness invading every part of her body?

'Put your arms around my neck and shut up!' he said tersely.

Having seen other couples dancing the same way, she obeyed blindly, feeling herself melting against him as he pulled her closer. As their limbs moved to the tender beat of the music she was aware of sensation flaming warmly until it almost registered pain.

Hearing a small sound of protest escape her, Ryan murmured, his lips against her cheek, 'You encouraged me when you called me darling. Did you mean it, or did you merely say it to annoy Angela?'

Melissa's blush must have betrayed her, but instead of pushing her away his arms tightened, as if to punish her. 'I'll have to see your motives are the right ones, next time,' was all he said.

There were more drinks at the bar, then Ryan announced they were leaving. Melissa, her legs still shaking from their recent dance and the fact that his eyes seldom left her in spite of Angela's blatant efforts to gain his attention, felt she would be glad to go. She felt suspended in mid-air, longing suddenly to have Ryan's arms around her again, to hear his voice, alive with soft threats, in her ear.

It was Angela who brought her swiftly down to earth, who spoilt what was left of the remainder of the evening. Smiling cajolingly at Ryan, she pleaded sweetly, 'Could you give me a lift home, too, darling? It will save Barry a detour and I know you won't mind.'

'No, of course not. I'm only too willing,' he agreed.

Glancing at him quickly, Melissa could see nothing in his smooth expression to suggest this was just tactful fabrication. He still cared for Angela, this was obvious, and Angela's ego didn't seem too upset, considering how she had found him dining with another girl. Her spirits sinking, Melissa knew it was going to take more than one outing to upset Angela's superb equilibrium.

It only added to Melissa's growing despondency when Ryan dropped her off first, especially when both she and Angela realised it would have been much quicker to have gone straight to Angela's home. Melissa, somehow or another, had found herself sitting in the back of the car and while Ryan did get out to politely open the door, he drove off again before she even got as far as the house.

That night she had great difficulty in sleeping and woke disgruntled to the strident ringing of the telephone. It was half past six. She had slept in. Mary wouldn't be up as she never came down before seven, but who could it be calling at this hour?

Racing downstairs, without bothering to wait to put on a wrap, she was bewildered to find the telephone had stopped ringing. Full of sleepy exasperation, she stared at it. She could have sworn . . . 'Oh, well,' she spoke aloud, 'I expect, whoever you are, you'll ring again later.'

'I'm still here.' Ryan's voice, laced with amusement, came from another direction. Startled, she swung around to find him leaning against the doorpost, regarding her lazily. 'I've just learnt you talk to yourself, a habit which usually points to some distraction.'

'Ryan!' she spluttered, not immediately remembering she wore only a brief, transparent nightie, under which every line of her figure was clearly visible. 'How did you get in? I heard the telephone . . .'

'You heard the doorbell.' The glint was still in his eyes. 'I wanted to see you for a minute and as you weren't to be seen outside I came here. I was just about to leave when I tried the door.'

Stupidly she stared at it. 'I must have forgotten to lock it last night.'

'So I found out.'

Mistaking his dryness for anger, she flinched. 'I'm sorry, I slept in.' Suddenly realising how she was dressed, she turned scarlet with shame, and understanding the quirk of laughter in his glance she rushed towards the stairs.

'Wait!' His hand was on her arm, stopping her on the second step. 'I haven't time to wait until you find something more—er—respectable to put on. What I have to say won't take a second. I just wanted to ask if you and your parents will be my guests at Poldary this evening. I should have asked you earlier, but we haven't been on exactly friendly terms and last night there wasn't the opportunity.'

'Because of Angela?'

'Yes, because of Angela.'

Melissa's eyes, level with his as she stood two stairs above him, riveted slowly, full of confused uncertainty. 'Will Angela be there?'

'Yes,' he exclaimed impatiently, 'I don't suppose anything would keep her away, but she doesn't have a thing to do with you.'

He couldn't have put it more clearly! 'I'm not bothered about her,' Melissa said stiffly, 'but I believe Mum and Lewis have friends coming in.'

'Then you must come yourself.'

'I ...'

'Melissa!'

Before she could retreat his arms went around her, the look on his face indicating that he recalled other times. Caught off balance, the whole of her slight weight fell against him and a startled cry escaped her. Surprise took her by the throat. Her heart pounded, shaking her body, and she guessed he could feel it. Was it this, she wondered breathlessly, which made his arms tighten and one of his hands to slip urgently into the front of her nightdress, to seek the tautly responsive fullness of her breast?

'See what you're driving me to?' he whispered huskily, as his mouth crushed her damp lips. 'Can't you just say yes, woman? You understand I have to get out of here?'

'Why?' She barely recognised the wanton invitation in her own voice.

'Oh, God!' he groaned, the pressure of his hands deepening punishingly, 'do you need to ask?' Like a man with little control left he stared down at her, as she lay submissive in the circle of his arms. Her hair was tumbled her skin sleep-flushed, her mouth as dewy and innocent as a child's. Then, as if tried beyond endurance, he was pulling the thin straps from her shoulders until she was almost naked, then his mouth took over again.

Against the seeking urgency of his lips she seemed to have no defence, nor was she sure she looked for any as everything inside her seemed to explode. She felt like the sudden eruption of a sleeping volcano. His mouth ravaged and explored, the impatience of his leashed ardour carrying her away. There wasn't a part of her he didn't seem to touch as he swept her to ever more dizzying heights.

'I'd like to take you upstairs and sleep with you.' His lips were hot against her throat, teasing her mouth, whispering in her ear, 'I wish your parents were anywhere but here. You're very desirable, and I want you.'

Melissa wasn't sure what she might have answered if a door hadn't banged shut above them. Probably Mary in the bathroom, but it was enough to jerk Ryan's arms away.

'See what I mean?' he muttered, the desire fading only slowly from his eyes as he saw how Melissa could scarcely steady herself against the banister. 'Here,' with dark deliberation he turned to her, throwing her a light coat from a peg in the hall, 'you'd better put that on or I'll have Lewis at Poldary, asking my intentions.'

Wordlessly Melissa accepted the coat, dazedly watching Ryan walk to the door as she belted it tightly around her. Before disappearing he spoke over his shoulder. 'Don't forget tonight. I'll expect you around seven.'

After he had gone Melissa trailed weakly upstairs. Mary was still in the bathroom and rather than wait she sluiced her hot face in the basin in her room, in an effort to pull herself together. She continued to feel slightly giddy as she dried herself before the window and took great gulps of the fresh morning air. Suddenly her heart felt as heavy as the grey, distant sea. It came to her devastatingly that she loved Ryan. She had felt it downstairs, as his passion had swept over her, but

it wasn't until this moment that she fully realised. She
had committed the great folly of falling in love with
Ryan Trevelyan, the man she had set out to cheat and
trick, a man who loved another girl!

Bleakly she wandered back over the room to stare at
her white face in the mirror. How could this have happened to her—hadn't an unkind fate done enough
already? And it was difficult to understand how she
could love any man when she didn't like being kissed!
Then she recalled how, last night, Ryan's light caresses
had become not something to be endured but enjoyed,
craved for, even reciprocated, perhaps nervously but
not without a certain eagerness. If she hadn't been so
consumed by thoughts of revenge, she might have read
the danger signals and guessed. Somehow she might
have prevented this happening. She need not have
gone out with him. She could have insisted on leaving,
produced some plausible excuse involving Helen, and
gone back to live with her. Even now, this was perhaps
the best thing she could do as the thought of seeing
him married to Angela was too painful. If she could
hint delicately that her emotions were in danger of becoming involved, he might be only too glad to be rid of
her. Hadn't he joked, this morning, about Lewis coming to Poldary to ask his intentions, as if this was the
last thing on earth he wanted? Ryan was undoubtedly
just amusing himself with her while he probably waited
for Angela to come to a definite decision about marrying him.

A tear ran down Melissa's cheek as the pain of Ryan's
behaviour appeared to throw new light on her own. He
was right in thinking Helen had given her too much
of her own way. The knowledge that Helen had been
grooming her to enable her to marry someone like
Freddy had been a shock, but she should have profited
by the experience. Instead of allowing her hurt pride
to take over she ought to have been more grateful for
being able to come back here. She should have helped
Mary instead of playing idly around. She should have

been on her knees thanking Ryan for all he had done for them instead of contriving, in every way she could think of, to annoy him. Why, she had even planned to humiliate both him and Angela for no better reason than that he had sent her around to the tradesmen's entrance!

Her pride truly in the dust, Melissa sobbed quietly, so Mary wouldn't hear. She must try to find an opportunity to tell Ryan how ashamed she felt. If she couldn't bring herself to apologise to Angela, she would to him. And when their engagement was announced she must be one of the first to congratulate them, although she hoped desperately she wouldn't be here then. Somehow or another she must get away!

That evening, when she was ready to leave for Poldary, Mary came out to the car to see her off. 'Now don't forget,' she said, 'to tell Ryan we're sorry, but it was really too late to put the Herons off.'

'You've already told him about three times over the phone, Mum,' Melissa teased impatiently. Then, as Mary frowned, 'I'm sorry, Mum, you know I will. I'm not trying to be awkward. It's just that I'm not keen to go alone.'

'Well, you can't be nervous, not after all the grand places you've been to with Helen,' Mary smiled, waving while Melissa smiled back wryly as Lewis pressed his foot to the accelerator.

'Women!' he exclaimed.

Ryan, realising Melissa might find it difficult to drive in a long dress and fragile sandals, had arranged that Lewis should bring her to Poldary that evening and he would take her home again later. Mary had thought it very considerate of him to want to save Lewis a double journey. Melissa would have insisted on driving herself, even though the reasons against it were valid, but she had realised that if Ryan drove her home she would have an ideal chance of confessing her duplicity and of persuading him to allow her to leave the holding.

Lewis dropped her off and she stood watching the

departing car with a strange sense of loss. Now she felt deserted, on her own, with no one to turn to if things went wrong. Wryly she considered how her feelings towards Lewis had gradually changed, and she knew a deep regret she had stayed away so long. No longer did she think of him as the stranger who had stolen her mother.

The door of Poldary opened as Ryan hurried out, immediately diverting her thoughts. 'I could rely on you,' he commented dryly, 'to be standing in my drive as if you didn't know why you were there!'

The old Melissa would have replied sharply that perhaps she should have chosen the back entrance, but the new, humble version found it difficult to even look at him. To see him again was to realise how the depth of her love could shake her and, at all costs, it was something she must hide. How often during the past weeks had she decided she had no pride left? It was only now, she knew, that it had really hit rock bottom, and if he was to guess, even slightly, how much she cared, she would never be able to hold up her head again.

Ryan took her arm, gazing down at her, as he guided her into the house, his eyes assessing the attractive picture she made in the deceptively simple new dress she wore. She didn't tell him she had rushed into town to buy it only that afternoon, hoping it would give her a little confidence. The creamy white of the soft summer chiffon complemented the deep, shining tones of her hair, emphasising the wonderful purity of her skin.

'You're looking beautiful,' he said softly.

'Thank you.' Her voice was hurried and slurred and she could scarcely look at him.

'I'd have fetched you myself,' he went on, removing the light wrap from her shoulders in a gesture which, to an onlooker, must have seemed intimate, 'but I only just got in barely half an hour ago and had to change. I had a business meeting in Plymouth which unfortunately I couldn't miss.'

'I understand.' She was conscious of other voices in

the lounge as he steered her towards it.

His smile glinted, as he misunderstood, maybe deliberately, her sombre expression. 'You must judge for yourself whether I'm in a hurry to return to my other guests, or just too plain scared to linger with you out here. If I did the latter I might be tempted to carry you off somewhere and risk being blacklisted as one of the worst hosts in Cornwall.'

Her mouth twisted, too nervous to reply. Instead she said flatly, without any trace of the breathlessness he might have expected, 'I'm sure you don't want to keep'—she had been going to say, 'Angela waiting,' but suspecting it might sound bitter, or impertinent, she substituted, 'your guests.'

'Wait!' His hand tightened on her arm, preventing her going through the door, heedless of a disapproving Mrs Barr in the background. 'Is something wrong, Melissa? You look lovely, as usual, but rather pale.'

'Why, Ryan!' she managed to smile coolly, 'you have a better imagination than I have. Now do let me see who's here.' Aware that such artificial gaiety didn't suit her, she almost pushed past him, pretending not to hear the words he uttered under his breath.

It was quite a large party. Angela, of course, was there with her parents, along with a few of Ryan's tenants whom Melissa recognised—and Barry! She hadn't expected to see him here. Attempting to go to him, after Ryan had trailed her around everyone else, she found Ryan's hand still on her arm.

'Any harbour looks okay to a ship in a storm, Melissa, but don't go to him.'

Not trying to understand his reasoning, she whispered, 'Why not?'

His eyes crinkled but he replied quite seriously, 'If you do I know where I can find a pair of handcuffs, relics, I understand, from the old smuggling days, although I can't be certain my ancestors were always on the right side of the law. Maybe, like me, some of those old pirates fancied chaining their women to their sides.'

Melissa tautened. She knew others were looking and flashed him a reproachful and painful glance. All of a sudden she wanted to cry and had to remind herself that she had been doing that on and off all day. Was he trying to make Angela jealous? If so, did she owe it to him to collaborate? But, no. From the look on Angela's face she was jealous enough already, certainly far from pleased to see Melissa here tonight.

As if relenting a little Ryan went to find her a drink and, as soon as he had gone, Angela slipped to her side. 'I suppose you invited yourself?' she asked insolently, with a quick glance at Ryan's broad back.

'Do you really think Ryan would have allowed me to gatecrash?' Melissa replied smoothly, trying to will away the high spots of colour on her cheeks. Then, shivering, she remembered she must not antagonise Angela any more. 'I'm sorry,' she muttered unhappily, 'I didn't mean to sound impertinent. Mum and Lewis were asked, you see, and they couldn't come.'

'Oh.' Angela's surprise and relief should have been reward in themselves. Her face lightened; she regarded Melissa almost tolerantly. 'So you came instead?'

Mutely Melissa nodded. If the applying of half truths was going to help Ryan and Angela find happiness together, it might help make up for her own deceit. 'Is there anything I can do to help?'

This again, implying tactfully, as it did, that Angela was more or less Ryan's unofficial hostess, won fresh approval. Angela's smile was condescending but did hold a touch of new warmth. 'Oh, thank you, Melissa, but I think everything is in hand. Mrs Barr has been a great help, of course. Just enjoy yourself.'

The smile on Angela's face appeared to win Ryan's approval, when he came back with their sherry, more than Melissa's pale listlessness did.

As he sat by her during dinner, he asked curtly, 'What's wrong, Melissa? I wish you'd say. I can't very well shake it out of you, with everyone here, but I might later on, if you don't cheer up.'

'I'm sorry, Ryan.'

'Then smile!' He glanced at her with a kind of impatient intensity. 'Don't you want to make a good impression on your neighbours? It's rather a large party, I know, but I find it more convenient to ask a lot at once. I'm a bachelor, remember.' His mouth quirked sardonically when she made no reply. 'I thought you'd enjoy a chance to show what you can do.'

'What I can do?' Her hand shook and she clenched it on her knee, frightened he should see.

'That's what I said.' His glance struck her downbent face. 'Maybe Helen didn't concentrate solely on spoiling. You're wholly elegant. You're lovely enough to grace any man's table, to say nothing of his bed. While I'm dishing out compliments, you may as well have the lot. You'd make a wonderful hostess, one I'd be proud of, and a man who was sensitive enough could turn you into a very desirable woman.'

'Thank you.' She couldn't let him see how his low remarks disturbed her. 'I think you'd better pass me the salt!'

'The salt!' He threw back his head, his eyes gleaming with dark mockery. 'All that flattery, and all you can say is pass the salt! I see I must concentrate on someone who might appreciate a few flowery compliments.'

The evening passed in a kind of daze for Melissa. Ryan, for all his derisiveness at dinner, was never far from her side, but she did manage a few minutes alone with Barry, who offered to take her home. While she would liked to have gone with him she knew she must wait for Ryan. The last few hours had made her conscious that she must get away from the district, and the sooner she told him of her decision the better. She tried not to think of the other confessions she must make.

CHAPTER TEN

SHE wasn't sure how it came about that everyone was gone and she was alone with Ryan. Guilt stirred uneasily with a curious indecision. Perhaps Ryan had wanted to take Angela home? Perhaps she should have accepted Barry's offer and postponed her talk with Ryan until another time?

Glancing at him, she spoke her thoughts aloud. 'You must be tired, anyway.'

'Don't remind me,' he grinned, while the inner energy he emanated refuted his dry quip. 'Even so, I'm going to make some coffee before I take you home. Don't you feel like a cup?'

'Well, I . . .'

'That settles it,' he smiled again as she hesitated, again torn by the opportunities which seemed to be presenting themselves, one after the other, and her own cowardly indecisiveness. 'I'll go and get it.' A glint of something flickered in his eyes. 'Mrs Barr has gone to bed and I don't want you in the kitchen again.'

That seemed to say more than his mere words portrayed. Melissa subsided, with an agonised flush, deeper into her chair. Must he tease her continually with his half-hidden innuendoes?

His tall figure stayed with her, even after he disappeared to seek their coffee. He looked so handsome tonight, seeming to outstrip every other man in the room with his hard vitality. The other women had watched him, but Angela had seen to it that that was almost all they did. She had rarely left his side and Ryan, Melissa had noticed, had been very gentle with her. Leaning back, Melissa closed her eyes still sore from much weeping, hoping wearily that a moment's relaxation might strengthen her for the ordeal ahead.

How much of an ordeal it was to be she had no idea, otherwise she might have fled home long before she did.

Ryan brought the coffee in two earthenware mugs. 'I couldn't be bothered with cups and saucers and all the usual paraphernalia. I hope you like it as it comes.'

Melissa's eyes opened with a start. What was he in such a hurry about? Not that she minded a mug. They used them all the time at home. 'I must have dropped off,' she mumbled, taking it rather clumsily from him.

'A few minutes' sleep, and that,' he laughed, 'will make you feel much better.'

Nodding doubtfully, Melissa obediently did as she was told, finding the dark, steamy depth of the coffee easier to stare into than his eyes.

'Aren't you enjoying our improved relationship?' he asked abruptly, a frown replacing his smile as he looked down on her bent head.

'Yes and no.' Quickly she took another sip of the scalding coffee before putting it aside. Bracing herself, she got to her feet. 'Ryan,' she faltered, 'I have to speak to you about the market garden.'

His mouth twisted. 'Must you? I'm not particularly thinking of it right now.'

'Yes.' She had to keep a tight grip of herself, force herself to go on. 'Mum and Lewis seem to have recovered their old ability to work together, their old enthusiasm, if you like. They're fully in control, and even you can't deny everything's beginning to go well. They don't really need me any more and I'd like to go ...'

'Go?' She might have been asking for the moon.

'Yes,' she took a deep breath, 'that's what I said. Ryan,' she tried to elevate her eyebrows to exactly the right degree, to fix on her mouth the most careless of smiles, 'it seems crazy that I have to seek your permission, but you know how it is.'

'No, I'm afraid I don't know how it is!' His voice and eyes were cooling to ice. 'Before we go into it, though, might I ask what's brought this on, all of a sudden?'

Her mind reeling around a dozen possible excuses pounced on one. 'I—I think I ought to go back to live with Helen. I've—I've been thinking about Freddy ...'

'Freddy!' His mouth was a tight line of anger. 'You'd better think of something else. I'm not going to swallow that!'

Mutely raising widening eyes to him, Melissa attempted to reorganise her thoughts. The conversation wasn't going as planned. But before she could speak again alarm forced from her tight throat a frantic cry as his hands pulled her cruelly to him and the violence of his mouth hit hers like a blow.

To be held so savagely against him was to suffer pain, but if she hoped such a brutal assault would subdue the explosive anger she felt in him it was still there when he raised his head. 'Now tell me,' he grated, 'do you still dare ask to go?'

She couldn't think straight. In the distance, when Ryan kissed her, for all his brutality, she had caught a glimpse of heaven. Maybe this was the right moment to confess that she had formerly intended only to trick him. He might forgive, understand. Her mind muddled on in confusion. Didn't he love Angela? Wasn't he playing a game himself? Whatever happened she must hang on to her common sense.

'Ryan,' she muttered, hanging her head in terrible shame, 'I only pretended to change, to be friendly because my pride was hurt and I wanted revenge. Revenge on both you and Angela. Don't you see,' with a great effort she made herself say it, 'it wasn't because I—I liked you any better. Not then.'

'Revenge!' She might have hit him below the belt— even his lips looked strangely white. 'Bloody hell! And I fell for it, the whole cunning little act. Well, I'll be damned! I never thought the day would come when a slip of a girl would make a fool of me.'

Sickly, Melissa gasped, as his hands fell away from

her, as if she were vile. Could there be any greater fool than herself? It came to her, with the ferocity and unexpectedness of lightning striking, that there was one factor, a vital one, she had overlooked. Ryan didn't know she loved him and in her stupidity she hadn't allowed for this. Now it was too late. She couldn't possibly tell him, and it was the only excuse which might have been acceptable, lessened his wrath. His pride had taken such a knock she was aware he would never forgive her, no matter what she said. She had no explanation, couldn't produce one, and he hated her as surely as he would ever hate anyone.

'Angela,' she gulped, through a haze of black apprehension as his eyes took on a diabolical glaze, 'I didn't really mean to hurt her.'

This seemed only to worsen the situation—if anything could. Devilishly he raised his hand, as if he would have liked to have struck her, but swiftly controlled himself. 'But you have, haven't you? Without thought or caring for anyone else but yourself. Don't ever let me hear you mention her name again.'

'I won't.'

He ignored the frightened sob in her voice. 'No, you won't, because you won't be here!' He was plainly incensed as he stepped towards her, driven by the sweeping fury she could see in his face.

She shrank fearfully away from him, but this only incited him further. Grasping her shaking shoulders, he spoke between his teeth. 'You'll be gone, Miss Nose-in-the-air Grant! I've tried everything I know to bring you down to a normal level, but after tonight you might discover what it's like to have your pride dragged through the dust. The solution is so obvious I could kick myself for not having thought of it before!' His voice dragged to new distorted depths. 'Never again, after tonight, will you be able to boast of yourself as inviolate, superior and immaculate. You might very easily find yourself an unmarried mother, which would,

I guarantee, with a pride like yours, be the final humiliation.'

'No, Ryan, no!' But not even the frantic cry on her lips, steeped as it was in wild terror, was able to stop him. She saw, in one tear-hazed glance, before his hands went to her back, that she had driven him too far, too fast. Now she must be prepared to endure the harshness of his rage, because this was what surged through him. Something over which, for once in his life, he had no immediate command. It was as if all his baser instincts had been released and directed cruelly on herself.

Yet not even now, with his arms like iron bands around her, could she believe he meant her any real harm. His threats, which while brutal, and had her blood racing, were surely not to be taken seriously. In the few seconds that seemed all there was left at her disposal, she forced strength into her numbed limbs, trying to push him away. 'Ryan, please,' she sobbed. 'You'll only regret it!'

But her struggles were of no avail. Her tear-strangled words might have breathed the air to fan his anger-driven passion into flames as he crushed her to him. Ruthlessly he held her in the hard circle of his arms, his expression one of cold determination.

With a distressed cry she tried to resist the pressure of his hands burning through the thin chiffon of her dress, and blind panic washed through her when she realised what he was doing. There was a tearing sound as he dragged down the zip at her back so that in places it caught at her skin. Then he was dragging the dress from her shoulders, sliding it from her with an expert economy of movement. Her fragile slip followed and he was picking her up, carrying her to the huge brocade-covered sofa across the room, his hand going out to flick off the light as he passed it.

Melissa felt herself thrown down, half stunned, on to cushions which were far from soft, and through the ringing in her ears she heard his jacket hit the floor followed by the swift rasp of his shirt buttons. Then his mouth was closing possessively over hers and her head was swimming dizzily as he gathered her roughly to him.

At first she tried to fight him but her whimpers of protest were lost against his lips, the pressure of which he only deepened cruelly every time she attempted to speak. When once she managed to make herself heard he merely muttered thickly, telling her to shut up. When she tried to drag her mouth from his she found it impossible. His hands caressed her roughly, crushing her against him as he removed her last silky pieces of underwear like so many rags. But she had no time to wonder at his expertise in this direction. Weakly she pitched all her remaining strength against the insistence of his slightly roughened palms, but as sensation piled on sensation she was defeated by the force of her own underlying love.

'Stop fighting,' he exclaimed, his breath on her face as sobbing, she turned her head this way and that, trying to avoid the deliberately arousing movements of his mouth. 'It won't help,' he jeered, 'I mean to have you.'

'Not like this, Ryan,' her voice caught despairingly.

'Yes.'

'Ryan, if—if you'd loved——'

'What are you trying to say?' One of his hands holding her head, he stared down at her, his dark gaze smouldering with passion as he watched the flickering firelight playing over her. 'You didn't imagine I loved you, did you?' His smile glinted cruelly as he lowered his mouth to hers again. 'One doesn't need to be in love to enjoy this.'

Much as she wanted to refute such a statement she knew he wouldn't listen, and it seemed incredible that, though he didn't love her, that didn't stop her responding to him in exactly the way he seemed to want. As his fingers traced round circles on her breasts she felt her limbs and arms seeking to entangle themselves with his as her body went completely pliant to his touch. He aroused incredible sensations, sensations which she

sensed he shared as the pressure of his mouth and
hands grew more urgent and his hard body began
easing over hers. Half on top of her, he was crushing
her, and the blood flowed like fire through her veins.
Wildly she clung to him as she concentrated with growing desire on the tumultuous feelings rising inside her.
Vaguely she knew he was gauging the depth of her response, assessing that the right moment had come from
the softening seductiveness of her mouth, the way her
hands held him to her blindly, and the uncontrollable
trembling of her limbs under his.

'Ryan,' she was breathing now, as deeply and rag-
gedly as he was, at breaking point and not minding if
he knew it. Her hands slid over his cheek, moving
feverishly, seeking the hardness of his body, the muscles
of his broad back which felt as smooth as steel and just
as hard. 'Ryan,' she moaned, 'if you want me, you can
have me. You ...'

'No!' Suddenly, to her numbed surprise, he was pulling himself ruthlessly away from her and she heard his
throat rasp, as though even such a small movement
had caused him more effort than he cared to think
about. But when he spoke again his voice had evened
out to its usual cool tones.

'No. Although you'd like that, wouldn't you? What
a crazy fool I'd have been to play right into your
hands! You would enjoy it, wouldn't you, to be able
to come back and sit on my doorstep, and embarrass
me? Even if your story might take some proving.'

'Darling!' his harshness went unheard as she tried to
pull his head down again, the urgency of her fully
aroused emotions crushing out every sensible thought.
'Ryan, I said I didn't mind what you do ...'

For one earth-shattering moment, as his hot gaze
pierced hers, she thought he was going to start making
love to her again, but his mouth simply hardened deliberately as he rolled away from her.

'Get your clothes on,' he ordered grimly, his eyes
flicking insolently over the whole quivering length of

her, as she lay curled like some small bereft Venus against the cushions. As he picked up his jacket and shirt, he added, 'I'll be waiting outside. You'll be home in ten minutes and gone, I hope, by tomorrow.'

Feeling worse than she could ever remember, Melissa dressed as best she could in the torn remnants of her clothing, but unable to face Ryan she ran out through the kitchen. She would walk home; never again would she accept a lift from Ryan, trust herself near him!

Quickly she let herself out the back door, only to find him sitting in his car, waiting.

'Get in,' he ordered, as she spun like a startled young fawn away from him. 'If you don't I'll get out and throw you in. Take your choice, Melissa. You see, I guessed what you would do.'

Shaken and silent, she sank weakly beside him, unable to speak as he drove her home. His face was hard and his use of gears and accelerator reflected the violence still within him. He would never forgive her.

At the smallholding he sat while she fumbled helplessly with the car door and, after a quick, indifferent glance at her white, tear-stained face, he leant impatiently across her to open it. The faint pressure of his arm was almost too much, but he might have been made of stone for all the effect it seemed to have on him.

'Goodnight!' he said savagely, as she stumbled wordlessly out. 'And I sincerely hope it's goodbye!'

Again without speaking, Melissa nodded, as she tore herself away from the bleakness of his eyes, not realising until next morning that it couldn't be goodbye. It was while she was throwing a few necessities into a suitcase that she suddenly knew she couldn't leave her mother again. Not like this, and not right away. In spite of what she told Ryan, she knew it was too soon, or too late, she wasn't sure which. Mary still needed her help, or perhaps just for her to be there, and whatever Melissa did it could make no difference to the situation between Ryan and herself now. If she stayed near him the punishment would be for herself alone. He had told her to go, but he couldn't really care, one way or another. Hadn't his cruelty, last night at Poldary, demonstrated his hate? At the end of summer, when the market garden was really on its feet again, she would leave and take a job somewhere, but until then, she owed it to Mary and Lewis to stay here. How often had she heard Mary saying very little help in business was as satisfactory as one's own family, and Melissa knew, without feeling proud of herself, that the way she had worked over the last few weeks would make her almost impossible to replace.

Wearily, as she began putting her clothes back in the drawers, her mind went back to what she thought of now as her battle with Ryan. She had been the instigator and the loser, and was suffering more than she had ever thought possible, but maybe she had learnt a few things as well. Hadn't Ryan taught her, if in a somewhat ruthless fashion, that there was more to life than having her own way, than considering only herself? Inadvertently he had proved how wrong she had been about Mary and Lewis, at any rate he had shown her how nothing was ever completely black or white. And he had removed all her muddled inhibitions about kissing a man, even if he didn't know he was the only man she wanted to kiss. He had brought her down, as he had said, to a more normal level and, for all the painfulness of the process, she felt somehow immeasurably better. As if she had, at last, completely grown up and, apart from the very real anguish in her heart, was a new person.

Yet the memory of what had happened before he had brought her home last night couldn't be viewed in a better light. In setting out to trick Ryan she had only managed to trick herself. Her stumbling explanations had gone wrong from the beginning, and she couldn't altogether condemn his subsequent actions. She hadn't found it possible to confess that she loved him, which might have made him more understanding. Perhaps, though, it was just as well as hadn't he made it abundantly clear he didn't love her, didn't want anything more to do with her. Tears welled, falling unchecked down her cold cheeks as she worked, as she recalled how she had responded to him. But this didn't seem so bad as what he had intended doing to her and his seemingly worse reason for rejecting her.

She was in the greenhouses, later that same day, when Ryan walked in with Angela. Mary had taken a phone call from him in the middle of the morning but only replied, when Melissa asked what it had been about, that it concerned a new delivery of compost and fertiliser. Melissa suspected it might have been to find out if she was still here and, while her mouth set stubbornly against the ensuing hurt, she felt unhappily grateful that he hadn't come to enquire in person.

Now, as she saw him entering the greenhouse with Angela clinging to his arm, her whole world seemed to crumble. He spoke to Lewis but not to her and, after a minute, when Angela wandered away to browse among the huge variety of pot plants Lewis was cultivating, he went after her, placing his arm lightly around her waist as together they bent over a fly-catcher plant which appeared to intrigue her.

Melissa felt her face grow white as she watched him smile, gently teasing as Angela lifted it up, laughing gaily at him, as if, Melissa decided shortly, the thought of hundreds of little flies being gobbled up was a subject for amusement. How could Ryan stand there and gaze at her so warmly!

Shaking strangely, Melissa wasn't aware how her unhappiness showed on her face as, for the first time, Ryan's cold, narrowed eyes met hers over the serried greenery.

'I thought you were leaving us, Miss Grant?'

She almost jumped. Having looked away for a minute she hadn't heard him approaching. Waiting until her nerves steadied, she raised her heavy lashes, feeling herself tremble again before his obvious anger.

'Whatever gave you that idea, Mr Trevelyan?' she found strength to ask sweetly, hating the wild colour which flared in her cheeks, much as she tried to prevent it.

As his mouth tightened and he took a threatening step towards her, she felt the dampness of too ready tears in her eyes. He halted abruptly, as she tried fiercely to blink them away. It was as if physically they had stopped him. He stared at her, her unnaturally bright eyes, the soil marks on her pale cheeks suggesting other tears had been rubbed off, then turning grimly left her. He paid Lewis for the plant Angela still held, then, taking her arm, without another glance in Melissa's direction, he left.

Thinking nothing worse could happen and that from now on Ryan would simply ignore her, Melissa felt alarmed a few days later when Ben rang her up.

'Hi!' he said softly, as she picked up the receiver. 'Guess who's calling?'

'I'm sorry?' She didn't have a clue.

'Ben, girl! What a blow to my ego. I'm used to being recognised.'

Melissa laughed, feeling startled but a little lighter-hearted than she had done of late. Ben's humour must be infectious. 'You forget I haven't talked to you on the telephone before, but it's nice to hear from you.'

'And it's nice to hear you say so,' he went on, before she could ask about his trip. 'I want to talk to you, honey, and I haven't much time. We leave again tomorrow. My old man's not too well.'

'Oh, I'm sorry.'

'I'm sure you are, honey.' He had the sound of a man torn in two directions. 'Ryan's giving us a farewell party tonight and insists I can ask whom I like. He says if I ask someone he doesn't care for he'll simply look the other way. If you'll come, Melissa, I'll pick you up about eight.' As she hesitated he pleaded, 'Please say yes, Melissa. I have important things to say to you.'

Suddenly, her tormented emotions subsiding a little, she thought, dully, why not? She wasn't likely to be invited to Ryan's home again and, if he intended to look the other way, she must just try to do the same. Besides, what possible excuse could she give Ben that wouldn't arouse his curiosity? Feeling caught in a situation beyond her control, she unhappily promised she would be ready.

Poldary being the last place she wanted to visit, feeling the way she did about Ryan, Melissa had to almost drive herself to shower and put on a flowery, sleeveless dress which she knew would be suitable for a casual occasion. Brushing her hair and applying a light make-up, she wondered why she couldn't manage to feel as cool as she looked. When Ben arrived she ran to join him outside. It was unlikely, after tonight, that they would meet again, so there didn't seem much point in asking him in.

'I'd like you to visit us in Australia,' he began abruptly, immediately he had turned the car. 'As soon as Dad's better I'll send for you.'

His proposal startled her nearly as much as his apparent assumption that she would jump at the chance. Where had his confidence come from? Had Ryan hinted she was an opportunist? She wouldn't put it past him! She glanced at Ben blankly. She wasn't sure why he was inviting her to his home, but she had no intention of accepting. 'Ben, I'm sorry, but I don't think I can.'

Her desire to soften the blow by not being too emphatic was wasted effort. He ignored it. 'I think I've fallen in love with you, Melissa, so you can't refuse to come.'

'Oh, don't, Ben!' There was a sudden sob in her voice because it couldn't have been Ryan saying this. 'You must understand,' she lifted imploring eyes to his face, 'I don't—I mean, I can't ...'

He put a quick, silencing hand over hers, his face despondent. 'You mean there's someone else?'

'There could be.' The words seemed to drag reluctantly from her.

'Ryan?'

'Please!' Surprise stunned her that he had guessed, but thank goodness, that was all it could be. 'Ryan and I don't get on.'

Ben considered this while taking care not to look at her too closely. 'I guess I've got the rest of the evening to make you change your mind. Promise me you'll take time to consider it?' he said earnestly.

Melissa felt Ryan's cold eyes on her as soon as she entered the room with Ben. Angela, looking beautiful in slinky black, was in her usual position by his side. How much longer, Melissa wondered unhappily, before their engagement was announced? She was surprised at the number of people there. Ryan was certainly giving his Australian friends a good send-off. Ben had shown her the buffet supper in the dining room and she recognised the local catering firm who specialised in luxury foods, but somehow the lavishly spread tables, the flowing wine, didn't tempt her.

Ben was determined to stay with her for the whole of the evening, but he did have to pay some attention to a few of the other girls. The floor had been cleared for dancing to the record player and one of these aspiring females claimed him. Relieved, Melissa sat talking to one of Ben's sisters, her back turned determinedly towards Ryan.

'Ben thinks Ryan might announce his engagement tonight,' Ben's sister whispered in her ear. 'Do you think so?'

Melissa found herself trembling. It had been one thing to think this herself, but another to have it actually put into words. 'You're—I mean Ben is probably right,' she replied unevenly—

'They look well together, don't they?' The girl sounded wistful.

'Yes.' Melissa was forced to glance to where they circled the room. Ryan, dressed casually in a pair of

light summer pants and a short-sleeved shirt, his face
oddly set for that of a lover. As if he sensed her gaze, his
eyes flicked to meet hers, his seeming to cut right
through her. Stricken, she glanced away, aware that she
couldn't bear much more of such pain with equanimity.

'My dance, I believe.' Panic rioted through her as
she found Ryan standing suddenly before her. Why
was he asking her, after all he had said? Foolishly she
shook her head. 'I'm sorry, I'm too tired.'

'Come on.' Taking no notice of her feeble protest, he
almost dragged her up on to the floor, into his arms.
His movements might have been almost savage for all
the care he took. 'I asked you to dance,' he snapped. 'If
you choose to be my guest then you must be prepared
to put up with such inconveniences.'

'I only came because Ben asked me.' She tried to
stiffen away from his demanding body.

'Don't get any ideas about him,' Ryan's mouth
twisted insultingly. 'He's only a couple of years older
than you and not ready to take girls seriously.'

Ryan's jeering tones stung her so badly she exclaimed impulsively, 'He wants me to go to Australia!'

'And you're going, of course?' The smothered rasp of
his taunting conclusion hurt more than the merciless
grip on her shoulders.

She would loved to have said yes, she almost did, but
realised in time Ryan might confront Ben with it, and
she had no heart for further complications. 'Mind your
own damned business!' She kept her voice low, letting
her eyes express her contempt.

He said tightly, as if he should liked to have hit her,
'When I told Ben he could ask who he liked I thought
you would be gone.'

'I changed my mind.'

'Why?'

Terrified of the leashed viciousness in his voice, she
whispered hoarsely, 'I don't have to answer any more of
your questions!' Using every bit of strength she could
find, she tore herself out of his arms, almost running

from him across the room to seek the sanctuary of a bathroom upstairs.

She wasn't sure whether she sat on the edge of the bath for minutes or hours, but when she crept down again the hall was quiet. The noise of music and laughter coming from the lounge made her feel sick. She couldn't go back in there, to endure more of Ryan's oppressive glances and Ben's repeated declarations of love. He couldn't be in any doubt that she didn't return his affection—hadn't she told him several times? It would be better for everyone if she slipped quietly away. She could walk back home, it was a mere four miles, and the night was warm, if wet. She had noticed plenty of rubber boots in the back store-rooms when she delivered vegetables; it would be easy to borrow a pair of those.

Walking silently along the heavy carpeting, she was passing the open door of Ryan's study when she caught sight of Angela in his arms.

Shocked to the core, Melissa came to a sudden halt, her face a ghastly shade of white, although she wasn't aware of it. All she felt was the coldness of shock in every part of her, threatening to take her senses away. Angela had her arms around his neck, clinging to him, as Melissa stood frozen, Ryan, as if sensing an audience, raised his head. For what seemed the hundredth time that evening, their eyes met and held, until with an audible moan of anguish Melissa turned and ran.

Instinctively she must have thrust her feet into a pair of boots on her way out, but she could never remember afterwards pausing to put them on. Pain tormenting every inch of her shaking body, she ran wildly away from Poldary, sobbing as she wondered why her first and last visits should be so beset by drama. In the distance she imagined she heard a faint shout, but the blood thundered so heavily in her head, she couldn't be sure. After that there was only silence, apart from the heavy, sobbing breath which seemed to come from her trembling lips.

Nervous that someone might try to come after her, she tried to keep parallel to the road, taking advantage of the moonlight when it managed to flicker through the grey rain clouds. It was dark and the paths which had been so familiar to her as a child were not so familiar now. Stumbling over walls and hedges, tearing her clothes and skin in the process, she realised bitterly that she had forgotten the best places to pass. Yet no physical hurt could be greater than that which she had felt on seeing Angela in Ryan's arms.

Eventually she came to the road again, some half mile from the holding, and was relieved to find no traffic behind her. The road was deserted, other than one approaching vehicle. The lane was too narrow here to avoid detection, so she bent her head until the car passed. Then suddenly she screamed, as the headlights seemed to hit her, blinding her completely as the driver swung abruptly over and slammed on his brakes. He stopped a yard from where she was, but it seemed much nearer to the girl who stood trembling in front of him, the despair and unhappiness on her face clearly illuminated in the glare of yellow lights.

'Melissa!' Ryan crashed out of the car as she swayed, catching her in his arms as waves of dizziness washed over her. 'My love!' his voice was hoarse as he gathered her closely to him, 'where in heaven's name have you been? I've been up and down this road a dozen times. Never do that to me again or I might kill you!'

'Ryan.' It was all she could get out as she clung to him, but it didn't seem to matter as his arms lifted her gently and he put her in the car beside him. Easing completely on to the grass verge, he switched on the inside light, his eyes going over her gently, taking in her torn clothes and the paleness of her face. 'I seem to have been responsible for a lot of damage lately,' he exclaimed harshly.

'I'm sorry, Ryan.' Overwrought, she felt tears beginning to stream down her cheeks again, but when she attempted to brush them away his hand stopped her.

His voice was suddenly urgent. 'Look at me, Melissa! I think I know why you ran from Poldary as you did, and you're in one hell of a mess, but if you feel up to it I'd like to talk to you before I take you home. It's something which can't wait until tomorrow and I don't want to have to say it in front of your mother, although she's certain to know.'

'I'm all right, Ryan.' Something in his eyes seemed to be making this more so every minute. 'It was just shock.'

'I realise.' His face was bleak as his arms went tightly around her. 'I'm sorry about that, but if you'd stopped to look properly you would have seen it was really Angela kissing me. Maybe it's not something I should mention, but the situation seems to warrant it. I know she's fond of me, but she knows I've never been in love with her, or made serious love to her. I know what a mischiefmaker she is, for one thing! Tonight, though, I was just finding out what I'd known all along, that no other woman could arouse me as you do. I think I've loved you from the first night we met, and I'd never believed in love before. You were headstrong, full of pride and maddening inhibitions, but although I admired your spirit I never guessed what a handful you would prove to be, or the lengths I would be forced to go to keep you here.'

As his hand moved over her head, soothing her with a new tenderness, Melissa felt joy surge swiftly inside her, banishing the cold and despair of the past hour. Yet she still felt too uncertain to believe it possible he could love her. 'Ryan,' she shivered, burrowing her apprehensive face against his chest, where she could feel his heart beating almost as unevenly as her own, 'how can you love me when you only wanted to be rid of me? I remember distinctly you told me to go.'

'Darling!' He drew back wryly, his hand sliding to her damp cheek, his thumb tilting her chin so she must look at him. Suddenly he bent his head and his mouth crushed hers, his kiss passionate and deep. She could feel the heat of his body through the thin material of her dress and the banked tension in him. 'You must try and understand,' he went on, minutes later when, flushed and bemused, she lay trembling against him, 'you are the only girl I've ever loved, ever wanted to marry, and for the first time in my life I found I wasn't in control. I seemed balanced on a knife edge and it didn't exactly help when you appeared to care nothing for me. When you said you were only playing a game I think I went beserk, but it didn't make me feel any better, after what I did to you. I found it didn't alter my feelings one bit. I couldn't have let you go, but at the same time, I couldn't see any immediate solution.'

'I'm sorry, Ryan,' she whispered.

'So you should be,' he said thickly, his eyes darkening. 'When I suddenly realised, in the study tonight, that you cared, I could have killed you for all the time we've wasted! I was so furious it was several minutes before I could bring myself to come after you. But,' he groaned, his lips against her mouth again, 'when I couldn't find you, I was punished a hundred times over for waiting even that long.'

'I wanted to tell you I loved you,' Melissa raised dazed, wonder-filled eyes to his face. 'After I told you how I had meant to trick you, but I couldn't. I had no idea you loved me, you see, and my thinking had got extremely muddled. I don't blame you for what you thought and was still trying to sort it out when you began making love to me. From then on I hadn't a sensible idea in my head.'

'I'll see you don't have many more.'

'Ryan darling,' she murmured, much later, as she floated on clouds of ecstasy, held closely to him, 'I don't deserve you. I was so spoilt. I could think only of my own troubles and hated you when you tried to straighten me out. Wouldn't it have been much better if you'd left me in the snow?'

He said tautly, 'I've loved you from that first night.

I'd never kissed a girl almost as soon as I met her before, but I couldn't resist you.' His mouth relaxed ruefully. 'I knew then you were fighting a few long-established inhibitions, and that you were too used to having your own way, but I never thought of you as being past redemption, my darling. I think I might have been as much concerned with my own fight for survival. Every time I saw you, I wanted to make love to you, to fill your ears with what I'd always considered pathetic drivel. But you didn't exactly encourage me, my love. You almost had hysterics, to begin with, anyway, every time I tried to touch you.'

Flushing unhappily, she confessed, 'That wasn't really to do with you, Ryan. It was something which happened when I was young, which caused me to leave here in the first place, something which, had I been older at the time, might not have bothered me nearly so much.' Faltering, she went on to tell him the whole story, marvelling, when she had never been able to tell anyone before, that it was so easy to pour it all out to this man who loved her. Nor had she dreamt he would be so understanding.

His mouth was tight, as if he almost felt for himself her young anguish, but he merely said softly, 'It's very easy to be over-sensitive and to judge wrongly at fourteen. Your mother, I believe, as I think I've told you before, is essentially a woman who needs a man behind her. Perhaps she wasn't being unfaithful to your father so much as seeking comfort at a time when she must have been almost distracted at the thought of losing her husband. Afterwards her hasty marriage might have sprung from the same basic cause. And remember, she hasn't had it all plain sailing. She almost lost you, and Lewis too, until he was persuaded to give up his gambling.'

'Ryan!' Melissa's eyes widened with sudden comprehension. 'Was it you? Did you ... ?'

'Shush!' he cut her off. 'The past is better left behind. I'll just say I helped him see sense. From now on your future lies with me. Not with the smallholding, or Cousin Helen.'

'She's gone off cruising. She was going to call, but never did.'

'In future,' he promised firmly, 'I'll deal with Cousin Helen. After we're married.'

'Then,' she stammered painfully, 'you still want to—to marry me?'

Ryan laughed, with a hint of his old arrogance. 'Why do you think I went to so much trouble to keep you here? If it took a little longer than I'd calculated, I'll just take it off the time I'd allowed to get you to church. When I insisted on helping your mother, I must confess it was you I was really interested in. Mind you, I do have an interest in horticulture, but you were the real reason I acted as I did. I had to keep you here, and very few would believe the lengths I went to to do just that.'

'Oh, Ryan ...'

His glance went over her, brilliant with intention. 'You'd better change that to yes, Ryan, and very quickly! We're going to be married as soon as I can arrange it, and spend our honeymoon in New Zealand and Australia. There are places there I want to show you. There's also a small retreat I have there, where all I'm going to do is make love to you.'

Clinging to him, Melissa could do nothing but let her wholehearted agreement show in her passionate response to his arms and mouth. A mouth which aroused an incredible surge of awareness to make the blood rush with excitement and urgency through her veins. She had never suspected such powerful emotions could dwell inside her, nor that Ryan would be able to bring her to such a pitch of response by his own unconcealed desire. His arms were like bands of steel around her body, his mouth sensuous on her lips and throat, and she gloried that for the first time in her life she wasn't frightened at being so close to a man. Ryan was all male and very dominant, she could feel it in the hard muscle and bone of him, the way his mouth claimed hers, the way his heart beat so thunderously strong against her own. Never would he let her run from him now, and she knew she would never want to.

'I love you Ryan,' she whispered, as he put her suddenly from him, as if her nearness was almost too much for even his self-control. 'I think I must have loved you for weeks without actually knowing it.'

He stared down at her flushed face, brushing his hand across her hot cheek very tenderly. 'On my island retreat I'm going to make you prove it.' His voice was soft but very determined.

'Afterwards,' she asked wistfully, having to force herself to think of 'afterwards' at all, 'we'll come back here?'

'Yes, my darling,' he placed a tender kiss on the tip of her nose. 'And you'd better be prepared to do the housekeeping for a while. Mrs Barr has decided to move on.'

'Oh, Ryan,' she smiled with sudden relief, 'you know I won't mind doing that. I ran Helen's house for nearly a couple of years and I believe I was rather good at it. My cooking, though,' she cast him a rueful glance, 'you must remember that! Mum did say,' she added hastily, as she met the amused glint in his eyes, 'I'm improving.'

'We can always get another cook,' he promised. 'In fact,' he threatened, 'I'll see you're much too occupied with me to have much time to spend in the kitchen. Later you're going to be kept busy bringing up the next generation of Trevelyans, but I want you to myself first, for a long time.'

Her eyes full of sweet confusion, a new humility, she swallowed a painful lump in her throat. 'I'll do everything I can, Ryan, to deserve you.'

'Melissa!' he tilted her mouth up, his own teasing. 'I don't want you too humble, my small fighter. I happen to like you just the way you are, with a little spirit. I haven't been exactly blameless myself and you wouldn't be the girl I fell in love with without it.'

Melissa sighed, trying to find the right words to explain how grateful she would always be that with his help she had found herself again. This, and so much more!

But before she could speak, he said, 'No more regrets, darling. From this moment on we'll just be thankful we found each other and discovered our love.'

And as her arms went once more around his neck and he drew her closer she knew, with stars in her eyes, she could never argue with that!

What readers say about Harlequin Presents

"I feel as if I am in a different world every
time I read a Harlequin."
A.T..* Detroit. Michigan

"Harlequins have been my passport to the
world. I have been many places without
ever leaving my doorstep."
P.Z., Belvedere. Illinois

"I like Harlequin books because they tell
so much about other countries."
N.G.. Rouyn. Quebec

"Your books offer a world of knowledge
about places and people."
L.J.. New Orleans. Louisiana

*Names available on request

MARGARET PARGETER

savage possession

Harlequin Books

TORONTO·LONDON·NEW YORK·AMSTERDAM
SYDNEY·HAMBURG·PARIS·STOCKHOLM

Harlequin Presents edition published June 1980
ISBN 0-373-10366-2

Original Hardcover edition published in 1979
by Mills & Boon Limited

CHAPTER ONE

'Want any help?'

The wind blew the dryly spoken words over Melissa's head almost before she had time to catch them. She turned sharply, as if the derisively shouted offer had removed some of the apathy created by the cold, whirling snow. The cold was so bitter it seemed to have reached her very toes, numbing them. It was even beginning to freeze her long, thick lashes, at least the damp particles of white flakes clinging to them, making it impossible for her to see the stranger beside her properly.

This was all she could make out, that he was a stranger. No woman could have forgotten such height, such a breadth of shoulder. He loomed so big she couldn't even see past him to perhaps ascertain how he came to be here? One thing was certain—he was too solid to be a wraith, conjured up from the storm and a too vivid imagination.

'I asked,' his voice, almost in her ear now, hardened curtly, 'if you required any help?'

Quickly she tried to gather her scattered wits. 'Even with help,' she shouted back sarcastically, 'I'm not going to get far!'

He shook his tall head, clearly not prepared to argue as his glance went flatly to the car behind her. 'Shouldn't you have had more sense than to venture out on a night like this? What on earth were you thinking about? Some girl, I suppose?'

Melissa drew a quick breath. So he thought she was a boy? Dressed as she was, and in such weather, it would be difficult to tell the difference. In spite of the cold and general discomfort she managed to suppress a half hysterical giggle. He could, this arrogant stranger, be in for a surprise.

When she didn't reply immediately he continued, in his overbearing fashion, 'You would have been wiser to have stayed by your own fireside with a drink. No girl could be worth getting frozen to death for.'

Melissa couldn't resist retorting, her voice as cool as the wind, 'That could be a matter of opinion, Mr—er——?'

He ignored her blatant fishing after his name, but he did take heed of her mockery. 'You have a sight too much to say for yourself, my lad, especially for one in your predicament. Were you trying to dig your way out?' He glanced contemptuously from the heavy shovel in her hands to the piling snow drifts which blocked the narrow country lane.

'I've got a flat tyre.' As if this explained everything she paused.

'So?'

'So?' she almost choked as snow blew into her mouth. 'I tried to change it, didn't I?'

'And?'

How easily his biting voice travelled while she had to use every bit of reserve in her long suffering lungs. 'I didn't succeed.'

'So I see.' He gazed briefly towards the jack, drunkenly inserted under the offside front wheel. His lips curled. 'The weather beat you?'

His casual disdain angered her. She wasn't used to hearing it in a man's voice, not when he was talking to her. She tried to remind herself he thought she was a boy, but even so she felt annoyed. 'I wasn't sure what to do first,' she hedged, thinking it wiser to hide her growing resentment, 'change the tyre or clear the road.'

'All you've done so far is block it,' he replied uncompromisingly. 'And I don't think you'll improve on your position tonight, no matter which problem you concentrate on first. Do you live locally?'

'Near the village.' She was suddenly, instinctively cautious.

'Four miles.' His eyes glinted with renewed impatience. 'That's too far. You'd never make it on foot and I have no inclination to face a round eight miles or so in this weather. You'd better come with me. I'm sure I can find you a bed, although I can't guarantee it will be aired, but even a barn would do you less harm than staying out here in this.'

A few minutes later, not wholly conscious of giving her consent, Melissa found herself lurching along in a huge, powerful Range-Rover. It seemed in spirit to match the man who drove it as it ploughed ruthlessly across the snow-covered moorland. She wasn't sure in which direction they were travelling, nor did she much care. Never could she recall feeling so cold. Even her senses felt numbed. The only warm thing about her seemed her temper. How dared this man, whoever he was, threaten her with a barn? Even if he wasn't aware of her sex it was an insult! One day, she vowed, if ever she got to know him better, she would make him suffer for this!

Then, dismissing such reactions as childish, she stared out at the pounding snow. How crazy she must have been to go to town on a night like this! It was quite dark now and, with the wind rising, the wipers could barely keep the windscreen clear. She had the sense not to talk; not even the certain knowledge that this would annoy her companion tempted her. It was six years since she had been to this part of the world, but she still remembered that the weather in Cornwall had to be taken seriously. To be caught alone in a storm on the moors could be much more fatal than accepting shelter from a stranger.

Snow still clung to her clothing, but she wasn't really wet, though she shuddered to think what she soon would have been like if he hadn't come along. Glancing at him sideways, she wondered again who he was. All she could see was a bit of his profile as a thick woollen hat was pulled well down over his forehead, but his mouth and chin were angled far too strongly for her liking. She preferred something less dominant.

The vehicle roared on like a lion until eventually they reached the shelter of a yard and stopped. Through the misted blaze of snow-covered headlights she could see a huge door, but this was all. After her rescuer switched off the engine the wind, screaming like a thousand witches, made her shrink back against her seat.

Her nervousness clearly aroused his impatience again. 'Get out,' he ordered abruptly, pausing with a heavy sigh as her numb fingers fumbled helplessly with the door. 'Here, let me.' His help might have been comforting if his manner had been kinder. His arm came over hers, his hand sweeping hers from the catch. 'Damn!' he exclaimed mildly, 'it's almost frozen.' The pressure of his arm increased over her breasts, seeming to sear her with fire under her coat.

As she stiffened in alarm she thought momentarily that he frowned, as if his subconsciousness suggested the impossible. Whatever it was, it was just as swiftly dismissed.

'Out!' He took his arm away as the door swung submissively under his hard strength and Melissa found herself standing knee-deep in snow.

Rather blindly she followed him inside. There was nothing else she could do, having no wish to be frozen at this stage by the very cold he had rescued her from. Apprehensively she wondered what he was going to say when he discovered she was a girl. It seemed too much to hope for that he wouldn't notice she was shaped differently from the boy he thought her to be.

She kept close to his broad back as he strode down a long passage which struck her as being even colder than it was outside. Seconds later he crashed through a green baize door into a large kitchen which was vaguely familiar. Melissa frowned as she stared cautiously around, hating to believe her suspicions might be correct. Her mind, in no fit state yet to jog a sluggish memory, fastened gratefully on the huge stove burning fiercely against the opposite wall. Heat was more im-

Great old favorites...
Harlequin Classic Library

Complete and mail this coupon today!

Harlequin Reader Service

In U.S.A.
MPO Box 707
Niagara Falls, N.Y. 14302

In Canada
649 Ontario St.
Stratford, Ontario, N5A 6W2

Please send me the following novels from the Harlequin Classic Library. I am enclosing my check or money order for $1.25 for each novel ordered, plus 59¢ to cover postage and handling. If I order all nine titles, I will receive a free book, *Meet the Warrens,* by Lucy Agnes Hancock.

- ☐ 1
- ☐ 2
- ☐ 3
- ☐ 4
- ☐ 5
- ☐ 6
- ☐ 7
- ☐ 8
- ☐ 9

Number of novels checked @ $1.25 each =	$ _____
N.Y. State residents add appropriate sales tax	$ _____
Postage and handling	$ _____ .59
TOTAL	$ _____

I enclose _____
(Please send check or money order. We cannot be responsible for cash sent through the mail.)
Prices subject to change without notice.

Name _____
(Please Print)

Address _____

City _____

State/Prov. _____

Zip/Postal Code _____

Offer expires December 31, 1980.

0065631

The **HARLEQUIN CLASSIC LIBRARY**
is offering some of the best in romance
fiction—great old classics from our early
publishing lists.

On the following page is a coupon with which
you may order any or all of these titles. If you
order all nine, you will receive a free book—*Meet
the Warrens*, a heartwarming classic romance by
Lucy Agnes Hancock.

The first nine novels in the

HARLEQUIN
CLASSIC LIBRARY